The Illustrated Library of

NATURE

VOLUME 7

FOREST AND
   MEADOW LIFE–(cont.)

FRESHWATER LIFE

INSECTS

The American Museum of Natural History

Cooperated in the publication of this edition.

The opinions expressed by authors are their own and do not necessarily reflect the policy of the Museum.

The Illustrated Library of
NATURE

᷑HIS PICTORIAL ENCYCLOPEDIA of natural history and ecology depicts the relationships of all living organisms to each other and between them and their environments. Original manuscript from the *Doubleday Nature Programs* plus new articles and illustrations are included in this edition.

H. S. STUTTMAN CO., INC., Publishers
New York, N. Y., 10016

Contents

VOLUME 7

FOREST AND MEADOW LIFE–(cont.)

WILD FLOWERS OF THE WOODS (cont.) 774
► *Flowers that live in the shade of the great trees.*

FRESHWATER LIFE

FRESHWATER FISH 792
► *Fishes we find in the lakes, rivers and streams.*

POND LIFE 824
► *The fascinating community of small animals and plants found in still pond waters.*

LIFE IN FLOWING WATERS 852
► *Animals and plants that inhabit our rivers and streams.*

INSECTS

WORLD OF INSECTS 888
► *The astounding array of animals that walk on six legs or fly with four wings.*

(right)
A member of the poppy family, the bloodroot of American woods grows in the same place each year. When the bluish olive-green leaves expand, they will be rounded and lobed, and at maturity they may be ten inches broad. The flowers open to form an eight-pointed star.

(below)
With scarlet petals so cut and jagged that they resemble flames of intense fiery red, the brilliant flowers of the **fire pink** are a striking sight in open woods and rocky slopes of North America. The plant has a long flowering period and is often used in rock gardens.

Climbing and Trailing Plants

CLIMBING PLANTS which are supported by the trees and shrubs of our woodlands are often beautiful and showy, both in flower and fruit. Among them are many varieties of *Clematis,* a genus of worldwide distribution. In the United States and Canada the virgin's-bower or traveller's-joy, *Clematis virginiana,* has sprays of white flowers and fluffy white seeds. The English traveller's-joy is a closely related species, *C. vitalba,* which often twists its woody stem high up into the trees and can form quite dense curtains covered in late spring with trusses of four-petalled greenish-white flowers. Its masses of long whiskers in autumn have earned it the name of old-man's-beard. A New Zealand species is *C. indivisa,* whose starlike flowers, more than an inch across, in a dazzling cascade, are also followed by "beards". An Australian clematis, *C. aristata,* has large solitary flowers.

The widely distributed genus *Rubus* includes such well-known fruits as blackberries and raspberries. Some species form bushes, others trail on the ground or, with the aid of their hooked prickles, sprawl over other vegetation, the stems sometimes rooting where they touch the ground. They grow vigorously, and often form impenetrable thickets; in Australia alien brambles have become a serious problem to farmers. Some of the wild species growing in North America are the black raspberry, or thimbleberry, *Rubus occidentalis,* of Canada and the United States, the western black-cap raspberry, *R. leucodermis,* and the British Columbian salmonberry, *R. spectabilis,* which produces lovely pink flowers, and even more conspicuous large orange-hued fruits. Most of the hundreds of closely allied British species are called brambles or blackberries. Their flowers range from white to pink or mauve, and the ripe berries are usually purplish-black. They often grow deep in the woods but then produce fewer flowers and fruits than they do in sunnier places. The native bramble of Australia, *R. parviflorus,* is a hairy trailing plant, but the most beautiful species both here and in New Zealand are the bush lawyers, *R. australis* and *R. squarrosus.* These climb high into the trees and bear long drooping

Numerous varieties of **clematis** can be found throughout the world, especially in regions that have cool summers. Many have large, showy flowers.

panicles of fragrant white blossoms and, in autumn, delicious orange-red fruits.

The tangled stems and sharp recurved prickles of the bush lawyers often make progress through the scrub very difficult, as also do a number of other Australian and New Zealand climbing plants known as the supplejacks. These include the wonga-wonga vine, *Tecoma australis*, which has clusters of creamy-white trumpet-shaped flowers tinged with pink, and with purple or darker red inside the trumpet, and the lianes *Rhipogonum album, R. scandens* and *Flagellaria indica* which make tangles of long lithe stems between the trees. The lawyer canes, *Calamus muelleri, C. moti* and *C. jaboolum*, are vicious climbing palms with thorns like fishhooks.

South African climbers include the leadflower, *Plumbago capensis*, with flowers of a beautiful pale cobalt blue, and the Cape jasmine, *Gardenia jasminoides*, with pure white blooms, dark glossy leaves and a wonderful perfume.

English woodlands are the home of two climbing plants associated in their common names but of widely differing families. Black bryony, *Tamus communis*, is a member of the tropical yam family with sprays of tiny green flowers and large dark heart-shaped leaves, whereas the white bryony, *Bryonia dioica*, belongs to the cucumber family and has starry greenish-white flowers and five-pointed light green leaves. Both have bright scarlet berries in the autumn. Another plant of these and other woods in the Old World is the ivy, *Hedera helix*, whose dark shiny five-pointed evergreen leaves on tough woody stems cover the ground or ascend high into the trees, clinging by means of small adventitious roots. The globose head of yellowish blossoms, fertilized by carrion flies and wasps, does not open until late in the year and is soon followed by black berries.

Many woodland climbers, like the ivy, will creep along the ground where there are no trees or bushes to cling to, and there are also a

(above)
Small, aerial roots make it possible for the **ivy** to climb upward and cling to the sides of houses and trees. Also known as English ivy, it has woody stems and dark, evergreen leaves.

(right)
The yellowish **ivy blossoms** are fertilized by wasps and carrion flies. Opening late in the year, they are soon followed by black berries.

A creeping woodland plant with oval, leathery leaves, **trailing arbutus** stays green throughout the winter. It has hairy stems and clusters of pink or white flowers. Sometimes called mayflowers, the blossoms open in the spring, filling the air with fragrance.

number of trailing plants which never climb. One of these is an increasingly rare plant of American deciduous woods, the beautiful trailing arbutus, *Epigaea repens,* with glossy leaves and clusters of fragrant white blossoms. The tough woody stem often runs considerable distances under the ground litter and the flowers and leaves grow so close to the ground that they are sometimes hidden under the fallen leaves. Partridgeberry, *Mitchella repens,* which trails its pairs of rounded leaves over the woodland floor, has white scented flowers and its twin red berries are eaten by game birds. The creeping snowberry, *Gaultheria hispidula,* has aromatic leaves, tiny bell-shaped white blossoms and shining white berries. A later-blooming gaultheria, the teaberry or checkerberry, *G. procumbens,* is a trailing plant with bright red berries which provide oil of wintergreen, used in embrocations and other medicinal preparations.

Trailing fuchsia, *Fuchsia procumbens,* is a native of New Zealand woodlands. Although it has no petals, its bright orange calyx tube with green, purple-tipped recurved lobes presents a striking appearance. The large bright orange-scarlet fruits are even more conspicuous.

The glossy evergreen leaves of the lesser periwinkle, *Vinca minor,* form a dense ground cover in many woods in its native Britain and in America. Long creeping stems, bearing pairs of ovate leaves, root here and there to send up short erect stems with pairs of leaves from whose axils lovely pale blue-purple flowers rise on slender stalks. These flowers open flat, about an inch across, and have five asymmetric lobes reminiscent of propeller blades. Bees and butterflies, whose long tongues can reach the nectar at the base of the tube, pollinate the flowers but fertile seeds are rare, and the plant spreads mainly by means of its creeping stems.

SEASONS FOR BLOSSOMING

EARLY SPRING

LATE SPRING

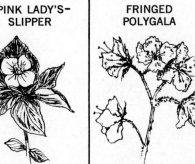
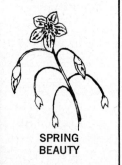
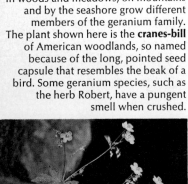

SKUNK CABBAGE

TRILLIUM

WOOD
SORREL

JACK-IN-
THE-PULPIT

DUTCHMAN'S
BREECHES

BLUETS

BRONZE
BELLS

WILD
GERANIUM

COLUMBINE

HEPATICA

PINK LADY'S-
SLIPPER

FRINGED
POLYGALA

SPRING
BEAUTY

GREEK VALERIAN

BUNCHBERRY

LAVENDER
WATERLEAF

In woods and meadows, on mountains and by the seashore grow different members of the geranium family. The plant shown here is the **cranes-bill** of American woodlands, so named because of the long, pointed seed capsule that resembles the beak of a bird. Some geranium species, such as the herb Robert, have a pungent smell when crushed.

WILD FLOWERS OF THE WOODS

EARLY SUMMER		LATE SUMMER	

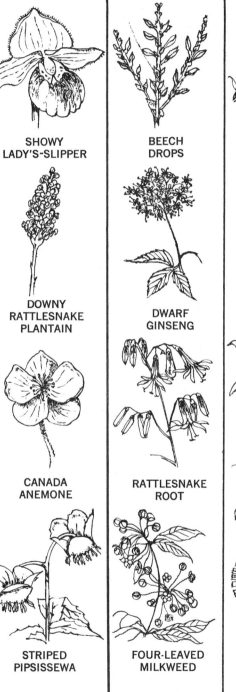

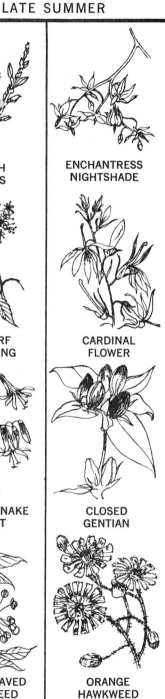

RED CLINTONIA

SHOWY LADY'S-SLIPPER

BEECH DROPS

ENCHANTRESS NIGHTSHADE

PURPLE FRINGED ORCHID

DOWNY RATTLESNAKE PLANTAIN

DWARF GINSENG

CARDINAL FLOWER

MONKS HOOD

CANADA ANEMONE

RATTLESNAKE ROOT

CLOSED GENTIAN

PYROLA

STRIPED PIPSISSEWA

FOUR-LEAVED MILKWEED

ORANGE HAWKWEED

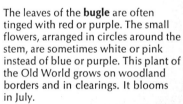

The leaves of the **bugle** are often tinged with red or purple. The small flowers, arranged in circles around the stem, are sometimes white or pink instead of blue or purple. This plant of the Old World grows on woodland borders and in clearings. It blooms in July.

(right)

Azaleas grow in many parts of the world, but most species are found in the Himalayas. The flowers, spread in clusters, usually have flaring petals and long stamens; often the blooms appear in such profusion that only a bright splash of color can be seen. This **pink azalea** grows in wet woods and swamps of North America.

Small yellow lady's-slipper displays its bright yellow lip and five twisted, brownish-purple petals and sepals. Like two other varieties of North American yellow lady's-slipper—one larger and one flat-petaled—it grows in wet woods and shady swamps.

Two other trailing plants of English woods are the moneywort, *Lysimachia nummularia,* and its relative the yellow pimpernel, *L. nemorum.* Long procumbent stems, rooting at intervals, bear pairs of leaves from the axils of which threadlike stalks lift golden flowers to the sunshine. The yellow pimpernel has pointed leaves and petals and the slightly larger moneywort has rounded leaves and chaliced flowers.

Honeysuckle, *Lonicera periclymenum,* is an English woodland climber that bears deliciously perfumed heads of creamy flowers with long reddish tubes. Though it is not a true evergreen, the plant is rarely leafless. The flowers are very rich in nectar, like the other plants that, in different parts of the world, are called honeysuckle. In America the pinxter flower, *Rhododendron nudiflorum,* is sometimes called wild honeysuckle, although it is an azalea. This azalea lacks the sweet scent of the English honeysuckle, but is a lovely sight in late spring with its rosy masses of blossoms on bare dark branches. Each bloom is about two inches long, deep pink outside, white within, and opens to disclose long curved stamens. Banksias, stiff bushes belonging to the Protea family, are the Australian honeysuckles. Their yellow flowers stand erect like huge cones, and are so full of nectar that a sweet drink may be made by soaking them in water. New Zealand uses the name for another protea, *Knightia excelsa,* which the Maoris call rewarewa. It has curious red flowers, like bottle brushes, growing on a tall straight tree. The honeysuckle of South Africa is the climbing Cape trumpet flower, *Tecoma capensis,* with long drooping sprays of large orange-scarlet blossoms.

Some Woodland Orchids

Woods and forests, particularly in the tropics, are the home of many members of the large family of orchids. Unlike the normal terrestrial species of temperate regions, most of those growing in the tropical forests are epiphytes.

Orchids are of great interest to botanists and horticulturalists because they have several unusual features. Their flowers take many different forms; some are just beautiful, but others are bizarre and resemble insects or other creatures. The readiness with which even those belonging to different genera will hybridize and give rise to new varieties makes them popular with plant breeders. Many are rare, or capricious in their flowering from year to year, which adds spice to the pleasure of finding them. The flower consists of three sepals and three petals. The sepals resemble petals and are often brightly hued; the two lateral ones, or wings, being alike, while the upper, dorsal sepal may be of a different tone, hooded or otherwise modified. The petals consist of a lip, or labellum, which is often very different from any of the other parts and may be variously lobed, elongated, spurred or inflated, and two others which are usually alike and may be joined to form a hood.

Among those with inflated labellums are some of the most striking of American orchids—the cypripediums or lady's-slippers. The small yellow lady's-slipper, *Cypripedium parviflorum*, has a rich yellow labellum, or "slipper", while the rest of the flower is brownish-purple with very long, twisted wings; the pink moccasin flower, *C. acaule*, is a small plant of the eastern United States and Canada with a pink-lipped brownish flower. Perhaps the most beautiful of all the cypripediums is the showy lady's-slipper, *C. reginae*, from the woods of Newfoundland and eastern North America, with large and fragrant blooms of pure white and pinkish, crimson-marked "slippers". In England the yellow lady's-slipper, *C. calceolus*, was once so common that huge bunches were sold in north-country markets; now it is so rare as a result of irresponsible picking that there is some doubt as to whether it grows anywhere at all in the wild. It is perhaps a century since these beautiful native plants could be easily found.

One of the spring-flowering American orchids is the showy orchis, *Orchis spectabilis*, with a spike of lovely magenta and white flowers, which grows in rich, mostly calcareous, woods. An early-flowering English species which belongs to the same genus is the early purple orchis, *O. mascula*, with a spike of purplish-crimson flowers and purple-spotted sheathing leaves. The lady orchis, *O. purpurea*, which grows in Kent, is a rare and lovely flower with a long pale pink three-lobed lip, flushed with violet or rose and adorned with long crimson or purple hairs; the remaining petals unite to form a dull purple hood. A single many-flowered spike may be as much as three feet high.

The American rattlesnake plantains, *Goodyera* species, grow in dry to moist coniferous and mixed hardwoods. Their tall dense spikes of creamy-white or greenish flowers rise from rosettes of dark ovate leaves that are often strikingly variegated. The creeping lady's-tresses, *Goodyera repens*, is a related English plant with twisted spikes of creamy-white blossoms which grows in northern pine woods. Twayblades,

Orchid flowers vary greatly in form, some merely lovely but others unexpectedly strange. In addition, new varities are continually being grown by plant breeders. Among orchids found in woods and forests, quite a few are rare, and many only flower irregularly from one year to the next. They all consist of three sepals and three petals, but one of the sepals and one of the petals are often very different from the others.

which take their name from their characteristic single pairs of large leaves, are found throughout the northern hemisphere. The small flowers are borne in slender spikes. In America grow the broad-lipped twayblade, *Listera convallarioides,* with greenish-yellow petals and purple sepals, and the heart-leaved twayblade, *L. cordata,* with purplish flowers. The latter species is also found in Britain, as is the greenish common twayblade, *L. ovata.*

Among the more curious orchids of English woodlands is the fly orchis, *Ophrys insectifera,* whose flowers have an uncannily flylike appearance. The wings are green, the labellum is brown and hairy like a fly's body and the upper petals look like tiny antennae. The night-scented flower spike of the butterfly orchis, *Platanthera chlorantha,* resembles a flight of butterflies, due to the widespread wings and pointed spurred lips of the greenish-white blossoms. The strange lizard orchis, *Himantoglossum hircinum,* which smells of goat, has a long forked and twisted labellum of greyish purple, with purple spots and furry papillae, and a dark hood. The resemblance to a small reptile is heightened by the small fingerlike lobes at the base of the lip.

Many of the numerous orchids that grow in South Africa are endemic to that country. One of these is the beautiful pride of Table Mountain, *Disa uniflora,* with lovely red wings nearly three inches across and a pink, scarlet-veined hood. It is unfortunately becoming rare despite official protection. There are many other disas; one delightful species is *D. graminifolia,* which has tall grasslike leaves and a spike of many small blue and mauve flowers. A number of hooded orchids also can be found in South Africa, including grandmother's sunbonnet, *Disperis capensis,* with several cream-toned flowers on a short fat stem, and the small kappie, *Pterygodium catholicum,* a similar plant with sweet-scented blooms of deeper yellow. A rare orchid from the forests of eastern Cape Province, *Calanthe natalensis,* is unusual in being blue. It has long broad leaves and a large spike of beautiful spurred blossoms. South Africa also has a number of epiphytic or perching orchids. These grow high in the trees, clinging to the bark, but they are not parasites, as they derive nutrients from decaying matter and bird droppings, and water from the rain. *Ansellia gigantea,* with a long spray of pale yellow and reddish-brown flowers, is the largest of these epiphytes.

Many beautiful epiphytic orchids grow in the forests of Queensland and New Zealand. Among them are numerous species of dendrobiums, whose flowers range from white to yellow and orange, from pink to magenta and crimson; they have large lips, often marked with spots and blotches, and wide spreading wings. The bird and cockatoo orchids, *Pterestylis barbara* and *P. vitatta,* are hooded terrestrial orchids with labellums so sensitive that they spring back at the slightest touch; any unwary insect that gets trapped within them can escape only by squeezing past the anthers and stigma, thus fertilizing the flower. The quaint spider orchids, *Caladenia* species, have fringed hairy lips, the remaining

Purple-fringed orchids grow in North American woods and meadows. The flowers have three-part fringed lips and are found in rather thick clusters.

This cluster of yellow fringed flowers grows on the **red goldfields gum,** one of the lovely flowering eucalyptus trees of Australia. There are over two hundred species in the genus *Eucalyptus,* an extremely diverse group of adaptable trees with blue-grey leaves and papery bark.

petals and sepals being long and thin like spiders' legs. The extraordinary donkey orchis, *Diuris longifolia,* with brown and yellow petals shaped like asses' ears, is endemic to Southern Australia. Lovely sun orchids, *Thelymitra* species, has showy flowers of pink, blue and yellow and grows both in Western Australia and in New Zealand.

Unique Flowers of the Southern Hemisphere

AMONG THE CHARACTERISTIC PLANTS of the southern hemisphere largely unknown north of the equator are the proteas, a large and varied family of nearly 1,000 species named after the god Proteus, who could appear in many different forms. They are mostly trees and shrubs, and are found particularly in South Africa and Australia, although some grow in South America; two in New Zealand and just a few occur north of the equator, in Japan. The chief genera of South Africa are Protea, Persoonia and Leucadendron, while in Australia Grevillea, Hakea and Banksia are predominant.

The national flower of South Africa is *Protea repens,* the commonest species in Cape Province. Like some other proteas, it is known as sugar bush because the early settlers obtained sugar from its flowers by boiling them to produce a syrup from which preserves could be made. Perhaps the loveliest of all South African proteas is the peach protea, *P. grandiceps,* with a fascinating flower-head of brilliant red showy bracts that enclose the actual flowers; these resemble pincushions stuck with roundheaded pins. One of the largest is the king protea, *P. cynarioides,* with an inflorescence twelve inches across which when fully open is like a bronzy-pink water-lily with a golden heart. The woolly bear protea, *P. barbigera,* has rosy-pink bracts edged with soft snow-white down and red edges to its grey-green leaves.

Occasionally these ghostly-white **Indian pipes** are tinged with salmon-pink. Saprophytes, they draw their nourishment from decaying organic matter. They are widely distributed throughout North America and as far away as Japan and India.

A specially handsome Australian member of the family is the waratah, *Telopia speciosissima,* the national flower of New South Wales. Its cone-shaped heads of densely packed bright crimson flowers are about three inches high, surrounded by crimson bracts that form rosettes quite six inches across and, like the flowers of the sugar bushes, full of nectar. The genus *Grevillea* is found only in Australia; its largest species is the Silky Oak, *Grevillea robusta,* a tree with graceful fernlike leaves and sprays of bright golden blossoms. Other grevilleas have flowers of pale yellow, white, orange or brilliant red which may grow in loose tufts, rounded heads or long spikes. Hakeas, or needle bushes, have stiff pointed leaves, flowers of white, yellow or crimson and dark winged seeds. Another very striking protea is the bull banksia, *Banksia grandis,* a large tree with great flowery spikes, often a foot long, of pale yellow tinged with pink.

More than two hundred species of eucalyptus grow in Australia, and nowhere in the world is there such a diverse genus of trees; it is so tolerant of different habitats that it dominates not only the woods and forests but the entire landscape. The leaves are usually a monotonous blue-grey, but the lovely fringed flowers grow in huge clusters. These may be yellow, white, pale green, pink or scarlet, and are most striking, while the shedding of the papery bark may show grey, red or even shining pink beneath.

Acacias or wattles are also typical of Australia and the golden glow of a tree in bloom is an unforgettable sight. More than two-thirds of the six hundred or more known species of acacia grow here, and they range in size from small bushes to tall trees. They are members of the pea family and usually have graceful silvery-green fernlike leaves and sweet-scented yellow flowers in fluffy balls or spikes.

Perhaps the most bizarre of all the native flowers of Australia are the kangaroo paws. They have swordlike leaves and the flower spikes, with blooms clustered at the top of the stem, are thickly covered with woolly hairs. The curved flower tubes, up to three inches long, turn back when they open, and then reveal their anthers which look like tiny teeth or claws. *Anigozanthos manglesii* has crimson hairs on the stem and calyx, and emerald green hairs on the flower tube, which is pale green within. There are eight other species, one of which has yellow hairs, one scarlet and yellow, and another, *Macropodia fumosa,* which is so thickly covered with inky black wool that only when the flower opens can it be seen to be yellow.

Parasites and Saprophytes

LIVING IN DENSE SHADE are the ghosts of the woodlands, plants which no longer use photosynthesis to produce their food and which have no green chlorophyll. Some orchids are saprophytic, and draw their nourishment from decaying organic matter. Many of these have queer twisted roots; among them are the bird's-nest orchis, *Neottia nidus-avis,* of British woodlands, named from its tangled mass of roots, and the coral root, *Corallorhiza trifida,* whose creamy-white flowers are to be found in both Britain and America. The most ghostly species of all is the phantom orchis, *Cephalanthera austinae.* Its stems, tiny leaves and large flowers are all pure, translucent white. Two other woodland saprophytes are the Indian pipe, *Monotropa uniflora,* which has white bell-shaped flowers and can be found in American oak and pine woods, and the yellow bird's-nest, *M. hypopitys,* which grows under beeches and pines in Britain.

All the broomrape family are parasites whose roots pierce the stems or roots of other plants, and live on their sap. The earliest to flower in Britain is the toothwort, *Lathraea squamaria,* which lives parasitically on the roots of hazel and elm and has short spikes of dingy white flowers. An American species is the beechdrops or cancer-root, *Epifagus virginiana;* this plant has tall branching stems of brown or magenta flowers and feeds on beech roots.

Interesting semi-parasites, which draw part of their nourishment from a host plant but also have green leaves of their own to help with food production, are the mistletoes, *Loranthaceae.* With the one exception of the Christmas bush, *Nuytsia floribunda,* of Western Australia, a small tree with underground parasitic roots, they are bushy plants which grow on the branches of trees. The best known is probably the mistletoe of the Old World, *Viscum album,* which can grow on many different kinds of deciduous trees. The white sticky berries ripen near Christmas time and are eaten by the mistle thrush which, in cleaning its beak of the viscid pulp, wipes off the seed into crevices of the bark where it can germinate. Mistletoe plays an important part in mythology and is one of the elements of the old pagan winter solstice festival that has become part of our traditional Christmas festivities.

When the white, sticky berries of the **mistletoe** ripen around Christmas time, they are much prized by the mistle thrush. After eating the berries, this bird wipes its beak on the tree bark to dislodge the seeds that have stuck to it. This helps the plant to germinate. Mistletoe is half-parasitic, drawing part of its nourishment from the plant on which it lives.

High Summer in the Woods

THE LEAF CANOPY is now at its thickest, with few flowers except the parasites and saprophytes blooming in the woods of the northern hemisphere. However in clearings, particularly those made by fire, the

Fireweed, or rosebay, spreads by creeping rootstocks as well as by its plumed masses of fluffy seeds. Always among the first plants to grow in burnt areas of Europe and North America, it has long, slender leaves and tall spikes of magenta flowers.

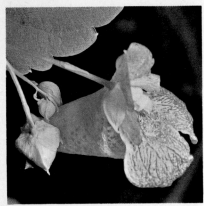

(top)
A common climbing **nightshade** found around thickets and at the edges of woods, this species has violet or white flowers with reflexed petals and yellow "beaks." Nightshades, which include deadly nightshade and thorn apple, are extremely poisonous. They belong to the tomato family, other members of which are tobaccos, potatoes and aubergines.

(above)
Like other balsams, the **jewelweed** is an annual plant that grows very rapidly. Its calyx and corolla are both orange, forming a trumpet-shaped spur. Its Latin name, *Impatiens,* is derived from the explosive nature of the seed pod, which bursts at the slightest touch and scatters the seeds far and wide.

rosebay or fireweed, *Chamaenerion angustifolium,* lifts its tall spikes of four-petalled magenta flowers with long slim leaves. When the slender seed pods burst they release clouds of long fluffy streamers to drift far and wide on the wind; when they come to earth the seeds lie dormant in the soil until suitable conditions stir them to life. This plant was once rare in England, but it is now as common there as in America. Another plant of summer is the American vanilla leaf, *Achlys triphylla,* with white feathery sprays of flowers and large leaves that smell very sweet when dried, and which earn it the name of sweet-after-death. In England the sweet woodruff, *Galium odorata,* is a small and dainty plant with tiny white starlike blossoms; its whorls of dark, pointed leaves, when dry, have a scent that accounts for its name: new-mown hay. Among the aralias blooming in America in June and July is the American spikenard, *Aralia racemosa,* with greenish-white flowers. The root of a similar species, wild sarsaparilla, *A. nudicaulis,* has been used as a substitute for the true sarsaparilla which is a smilax that grows in the tropical forests of Central America. Other aralias are the common dwarf ginseng, *Panax trifolius,* which flowers in May, and the rarer July-flowering ginseng, *P. quinquefolius,* with hemispherical flower-heads of yellowish green.

Many members of the Pyrolaceae, a small family found only in the northern hemisphere, are known as wintergreens, because their evergreen leaves can be found all the year round. Most species have rosettes of glossy green leaves and a single flower stalk that bears one or more saucer-shaped blossoms. The striped pipsissewa, *Chimaphila umbellatus,* usually has two shell-pink or white flowers and the stem is encircled by whorls of sharp-toothed elongated leaves with pale midribs. This, like the spotted wintergreen, *C. maculata,* which has greenish-white solitary flowers, grows in oak or pine woods. The shinleaf, *Pyrola elliptica,* growing in dry or moist woods, has white-veined leaves and an elongated cluster of greenish-white nodding flowers. All these grow in America, as does a small typical species with the charming name of one-flowered pyrola, or single delight, *Moneses uniflora.* Its single blossom, with five crimped, waxy white petals, which rises above a rosette of clear pale green leaves, is rather rare in Britain. Other British wintergreens include the tiny pink-flowered *Pyrola minor,* which often grows high on mountains; *P. media* is a little larger, with pink-tinged white petals; the largest and most beautiful, *P. rotundifolia,* has lovely blooms of pure white, in a slender spike of pendant bells.

The monkshoods, *Aconitum* species, flower in northern hemisphere woodlands in July. Although their deeply-cut leaves and tall spikes of dark blue hooded blossoms are quite unlike the familiar buttercups of the meadows, they belong to the same family, *Ranunculaceae.* The genus is very poisonous, and produces the alkaloid aconitin, which is extracted for use in relieving nervous pain. Even more beautiful, and certainly less deadly, are members of a related genus, the columbines,

Aquilegia species. Their spurred petals usually have the spur in one tone and the blade in another, while the sepals echo the hue of the spurs. The name is from columba, the Latin word for a dove, and the flower is supposed to resemble a nest of these birds. Only one columbine, *Aquilegia vulgaris,* is found in England. The flowers are sometimes pink or white, but more often dark blue or purple and, on any one plant, are always of a single hue. America, however, has many species, of which the long-spurred blue columbine, *A. caerulea,* is particularly lovely. This flower, with sepals and long curved spurs of lavender-blue and creamy-white petals, is probably the most important ancestor of modern garden varieties. The Sitka columbine, *A. formosa,* a plant of western North America, has large flowers with red spurs and yellow petals, while in the East grows the Canadian columbine, *A. canadensis,* similar in hue but not so large.

A summer flower of English woods and clearings is the foxglove, *Digitalis purpurea,* with tall spikes of purplish-pink nodding bell-like blossoms. The throat of each flower is beautifully mottled with dark spots, and their plentiful nectar guarantees the attention of the bees that pollinate them. The name is a corruption of folk's or fairy's glove. This very poisonous plant is a source of digitalin, which is used to treat heart complaints.

High summer south of the equator is Christmas time, and a number of different plants, flowering at this time in Australia, have been given the name of Christmas bush or tree in the various states. In Tasmania *Bursaria spinosa,* a spiny evergreen shrub with large heads of cream-toned flowers, is the Christmas bush, and in Western Australia a mistletoe, *Nuytsia floribunda,* which is parasitic on tree roots, has the same name. For a short period at Christmas time this shrub is a dazzling mass of flame, with six-petalled cadmium-yellow flowers crowded at the ends of its branches. The roots, searching for host trees, are said to have been found stretching for over a hundred yards. New South Wales has a Christmas bush, *Ceratopetalum gummiferum,* which grows to as much as fifty feet high. Although the narrow leaflets and small white flowers are inconspicuous, the sepals elongate and change hue

(above)
Because their flowers were thought to resemble a nest of doves, **columbines** were named after the Latin word for these birds, *columba.* Many species are found in North America, including the long-spurred blue columbine, the Sitka columbine and the Canadian columbine.

(left)
The **foxglove,** or **purple digitalis,** is a summer flower of European woods. Although it is poisonous, it has beneficial medicinal properties because it is a source of digitalin, important in treating heart problems.

around Christmas time, covering the bush with trusses of brilliant scarlet. *Prostanthera lasianthos,* with the characteristic lipped flowers of the Labiate family, is the Christmas bush of Victoria, and its pink-tinged white blossoms have purple-spotted lips. The Christmas bells of Australia, *Blanfordia* species, are beautiful lilies with hanging bell-shaped flowers of crimson, orange or yellow. One lovely variety which grows in Queensland is shaded from red to golden. New Zealand also has a Christmas tree: the pohutukawa, *Metrosideros tomentosa,* which ranges in size from a small bush to a large tree. Its stems, branches and the undersides of its leaves are clothed in a thick white down. The upper surfaces of the leaves are dark green, while the deep crimson flowers arranged in terminal many-flowered clusters make a tree in full bloom a magnificent sight.

Flowers of the Late Summer

LATE SUMMER IS THE CHIEF TIME for the flowering of those members of the Composite family that grow in woodland habitats. Golden-rods and asters now bloom along the borders of American woods and one of the loveliest is the giant goldenrod, *Solidago gigantea.* Each of its tiny flowers is a perfect golden daisy. The native goldenrod of English woods is a smaller species, *Solidago virgaurea,* but several American species are grown in English gardens and, because of the ease with which their plumed seeds are carried by the wind, some of them have become naturalized in British woods. Aster species have also spread from English gardens, where they are known as Michael-mas daisies—but more often to railway banks or waste places than to the woodlands. On both sides of the Atlantic numerous hawkweeds, *Hieracium* species, may be found. Most have golden flowers, but the devil's paintbrush, *Hieracium aurantiacum,* of open fields, which lifts its blossoms on tall stems from rosettes of dark hairy leaves, is orange-red.

One of the treasures of North American woods is the moisture-loving cardinal flower, *Lobelia cardinalis,* which bears fiery scarlet flowers in a foot-long raceme on a tall leafy spike. The blooms are each an inch long with two narrow upper petals and a long, deeply three-cleft lip. It is a member of the Campanula family, to which also belong several English species. The giant bell-flower, *Campanula latifolia,* of northern woods, and bats-in-the-belfry, *C. trachelium,* which is more often found in the south of the country, are two of these. Both are well worth finding, with their tall spikes of drooping blue bells and rough pointed leaves, especially the huge giant bell-flower which is often over four feet high.

The jewelweed or orange balsam, *Impatiens capensis,* grows in wet shady places. Its curious flowers, orange with brown spots or blotches, are followed by seed pods that, when ripe, explode at a touch and

Wet, shady places in North America are the homes of the beautiful, moisture-loving **cardinal flowers.** The numerous blossoms on the long spikes ensure a very long flowering period. They are fertilized by ruby-throated hummingbirds. A related species, the giant lobelia, is deep blue.

fling the seeds far from the parent plant. A native of America, it is also widely distributed throughout Britain. Another balsam, recently established in England, is the policeman's helmet, *I. glandulifera*. This native of the Himalayas, which was first noticed near the docks, has found the climate so much to its liking that it has spread along stream and river banks into the heart of the country and is now quite common. The large flowers, of every shade from pale pink, or even white, to deep pinkish-purple, bear a fancied resemblance, with their swollen corollas and hooked spurs, to the helmets worn by London policemen.

The Declining Year

IN AUTUMN THE DECIDUOUS WOODLANDS are ablaze with brilliant hues as the dying leaves take on many different tints. Oak leaves may be crimson or brown, maples and sycamores flaming scarlet or golden,

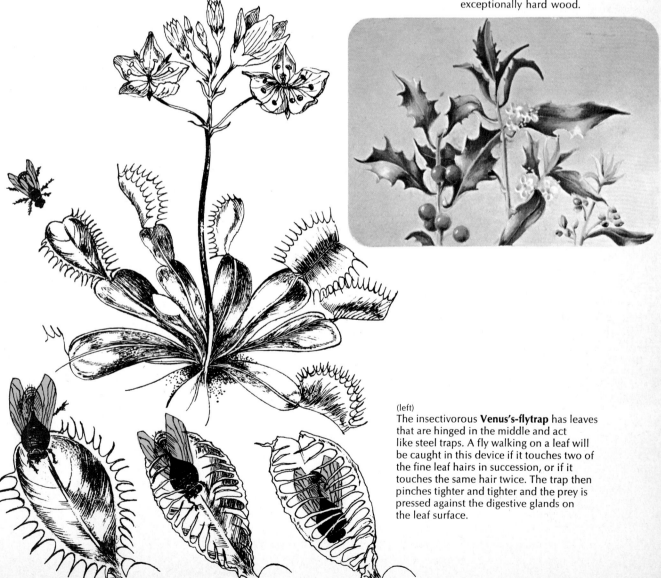

(below)
Sparkling red **holly** berries brighten the bleak winter months and make lovely Christmas wreaths. A healthy holly plant may grow to tree size, thirty to forty feet high, and have a trunk of exceptionally hard wood.

(left)
The insectivorous **Venus's-flytrap** has leaves that are hinged in the middle and act like steel traps. A fly walking on a leaf will be caught in this device if it touches two of the fine leaf hairs in succession, or if it touches the same hair twice. The trap then pinches tighter and tighter and the prey is pressed against the digestive glands on the leaf surface.

The natural range of the delicate
snowdrop, which blooms in the early
spring, extends from Britain to
southern Europe. In Wales it is known
as herb of the snow or baby's bell.
The three outer petals are pure white,
and the three inner ones are tipped
with green.

poplars, willows, chestnuts and birches all shades of yellow, gold and brown. The finest display is undoubtedly in the northern hemisphere; but introduced trees have carried this ephemeral beauty south of the equator. Wild fruits add to this brilliance and also provide a store of food for birds and other animals during the winter months. Berries of all shades of crimson and scarlet may be found on roses, hawthorns, bryonies, nightshades and guelder roses. Privet, ivy, elder and bramble have black berries and snowberries add a touch of white.

Soon the cold blasts of November pull the last withered leaves from the branches to fall around the red, purple, brown, white and yellow of the fungi, on the woodland floor. The holly, *Ilex aquifolia,* and the ivy, *Hedera helix,* "are both now full well grown". The prickly dark leaves and glowing scarlet berries of the holly, with long trails of ivy, will decorate the house for Christmas. With the tinsel-hung fir for Christmas tree, the mistletoe's glistening white berries as forfeit for kisses and the Yule log blazing on the hearth, the woods provide everything for a traditional Christmas.

Now the woods are held in the icy grip of winter and there is little sign of life among the plants and trees, but spring will soon return and even in these dark days a few brave blossoms give promise of future sunshine. In the bare brown woods of North America the long golden petals of the witch hazel, *Hamamelis virginiana,* twist and turn in the wind as if in defiance of winter, while in some English woods the winter heliotrope, *Petasites fragrans,* opens its sweet-scented pale lilac flowers. Soon the snowdrops will follow and the whole wonderful cycle of Nature will start anew.

FRESHWATER LIFE

There are no scientifically acceptable definitions that clearly distinguish between ponds and lakes, and perhaps the same can be said about attempts to differentiate brooks from streams and even rivers. Taken together, however, these bodies of water form the habitats of freshwater life.

Every pond, stream or river is unique; none is quite like another. Folklore, ancient legends and even mystical beliefs have always been associated with these waters, and each of us has his own personal experiences with them as well, whether of sport and recreation or of quiet contemplation. In the pages ahead we return to these settings to discover a world full of strange surprises: the teeming populations that inhabit fresh water.

FRESHWATER FISH, which include popular game fish like bass and trout, food fish such as salmon and carp, and favorite aquarium species like goldfish and angelfish, are the subjects of the opening chapter in this category. Also examined are many less familiar species whose names alone arouse our curiosity: flying hatchet fish and mudskippers, mouthbrooders and kissing gourami, archer fish and many others besides.

Even if it is hardly more than a seasonal puddle left by the rain, a pond is probably accessible to most people. It is therefore an ideal place to investigate a world in miniature of freshwater life, an illustrated guide to which is provided by the chapter on POND LIFE.

It may be said that the arteries, or the highways, of the earth are its river systems, which begin as tiny, rippling brooks, widen into fast-moving streams and join rivers—often swift and majestic—that flow to the sea. LIFE IN FLOWING WATERS follows this winding course, exploring myriad forms of life—from sponges, mussels and giant water bugs to crayfish, frogs and turtles—that are encountered along the way.

To all this one qualification must be added. This discussion presumes healthy, unpoisoned waters; yet nowhere else is the pollution of our environment more apparent than in the ponds, lakes and river systems into which sewage and industrial wastes have thoughtlessly been poured. If these chapters are concerned with waters that swarm with life, it is hoped they may make us more aware, and more ready to do something about, those in which life is endangered or already void.

▶ *Fishes we find in the lakes, rivers, and streams.*

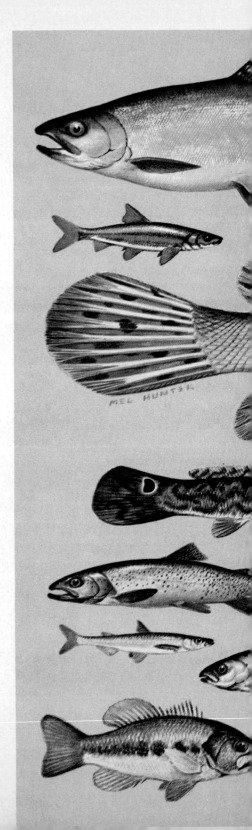

MEL HUNTER

Freshwater Fish

THE FIRST BACKBONED ANIMALS were fishlike but were related to the lampreys living today. Their most ancient fossil remains, nearly 500 million years old, are found in rocks laid down in the sea. But lampreys are not now regarded as fishes. The remains of the first true fishes are little more than 400 million years old, and these are found in estuaries or fresh-water deposits. This is not to say that true fishes originated in rivers; there is just as much ground for supposing they originated in the sea, since some of the many fresh-water families contain member species that are marine or estuarine. In addition there are the anadromous fishes such as the salmon that migrate from the sea to fresh water, and catadromous fishes such as the eel that migrate from fresh water to the sea.

For the last thirty years or so, it has been generally accepted by ichthyologists, that the cartilaginous fishes (such as sharks, rays and skates) form a separate group from the bony or true fishes. They may have had a common ancestor 500 million years ago; but since then each has followed a separate course of evolution, and the scientist speaks of the two branches as the class Selachii (cartilaginous fishes) and the class Pisces (true or bony fishes).

The differences between the members of the two classes are many, apart from the fundamental difference that the one class is characterized by a cartilaginous skeleton and the other by a bony skeleton. Furthermore, the Selachii are almost exclusively marine. There are a few of them, including sharks, sawfishes and sting rays, that will travel far up rivers but without becoming permanent residents. The Atlantic ground shark, also known as bull or cub shark, is known to go up the

Although fresh-water fishes vary less in size and shape than those of the sea, their breeding behavior and their method of breathing are often more specialized, and in some respects more fascinating. Mouth-brooders, sticklebacks and lungfish are good cases in point. In addition, some of the most important and popular food fishes live in fresh water, as do many colorful and exotic aquarium species. Among the most unusual are the **fresh-water hatchet fishes** (top right), the only fishes that actually fly, flapping their fins like wings.

(top)
Small characins, such as this **tetra perez,** are often called "tetras," and a number of the more colorful species make attractive aquarium fishes. The characins, a family of some 500 species inhabiting warmer waters, include the piranhas of South America and the African tigerfish.

(above)
In albino fishes, such as this **albino catfish,** the body is white and lacks pigment. Often the loss of pigment is not complete, the fish retaining patches or spots of black or brown, as in the black and silver varieties of goldfish.

Atchafalaya River, in Louisiana, to a distance of nearly 200 miles. This shark is a near relative of the Lake Nicaragua shark of Central America, which is the only permanently fresh-water shark.

The Lake Nicaragua shark is up to ten feet long and keeps near the bottom of the lake, but there are many records of attacks by it on human beings. The theory is that, like its less dangerous relative, the ground shark, it had the habit of migrating up the Don Carlos River and eventually found itself confined to Lake Nicaragua as a result of earth movements.

The Importance of Fresh-Water Fish

EARLY MAN PROBABLY TOOK FISH from rivers and lakes before he learned to exploit the marine fishes, and primitive peoples everywhere have continued to do this. In later times more attention was given to marine fisheries, especially by the peoples bordering the North Atlantic. Yet even there the fresh-water fishing continued, although often more as a sport or recreation. Moreover, since the start of the Industrial Revolution there has been increasing pollution of rivers by factory effluents and sewage, with the result that in western Europe and North America once bountiful rivers are now almost totally devoid of fish.

Elsewhere in the world, in areas lacking heavy industrialization, fresh-water fishes are an important item of food for the indigenous peoples, and efforts are being currently directed towards further exploitation of the fishes of large rivers and lakes. Experience has also shown that it is practicable to fertilize lakes artificially to increase plant-plankton growth, and thus increase the yield of fishes.

Another activity has increased the importance of fresh-water fishes. Never before has the keeping of home aquaria been so widespread. Whereas a few decades ago this was limited to a glass bowl with a single goldfish swimming interminably around, serious aquarium-keeping, especially of "tropicals", has countless devotees.

Specialization in Fresh-Water Fishes

AS COMPARED WITH MARINE FISHES the shape of fresh-water fishes is fairly uniform. In the sea there are fishes of the normal fish shape, but there are many others that are flattened, others almost globular, and a diversity of form between these two extremes. In fresh-water fishes there is less departure from the typical form. Perhaps the biggest single feature that is more pronounced in fresh-water fishes is found in the breeding behavior, with its greater emphasis on nest-building and parental care. There are also more examples of specializations in the breathing apparatus, a necessary adaptation for life in stagnant pools as well as in drought conditions.

The fresh-water fishes, also, do not approach the larger of the marine fishes for size, if we include the whale shark with a length of sixty feet or more. But if we confine attention to the true fishes, there are many in the sea that exceed six feet in maximum length, and a weight of up to half a ton. The largest is the swordfish, which may reach twenty feet and a weight of over half a ton. The nearest to these dimensions in fresh waters is the Russian sturgeon, or beluga, of the Black and Caspian seas and the Volga River, which may attain twenty-eight feet and over a ton weight. This is, however, one of the anadromous fishes, equally at home in salt and fresh water.

Fresh-water fishes include, by contrast, the smallest of all, a goby living in the lakes in the Philippines. This is only a half-inch long when fully grown, thereby earning the distinction of being the smallest of all vertebrates. However, this is an empty victory for fresh-water fishes since gobies are mainly marine, and the majority of those found in fresh water are catadromous.

Some Primitive Fishes

ALTHOUGH WE SPEAK OF TRUE or bony fishes, there are some which have a cartilaginous skeleton, as in the sharks, but the cranium is covered with bone. Moreover, although such fishes are clearly primitive in their skeleton, they are advanced in the structure of their gills. In the sharks the gills open at the surface of the body with individual gill clefts, but in all bony fishes, including these primitive species, the gill arches with their filaments are covered with a flap, or operculum. In the primitive species, also, there is an air bladder, which functions as a kind of lung.

(above)

Goldfish have been selectively bred for centuries, resulting in a wide variety of shapes and hues. The earliest records of goldfish date from A.D. 970. In sixteenth century China it was a widespread practice to keep them in bowls and garden pools, and in the seventeenth century they were brought to Europe by the Portuguese. In this picture the fish shown is the **lionhead goldfish.**

(left)

One of the smaller sturgeons, the **shovelnosed sturgeon** of the central United States feeds on water snails, insect larvae, crayfish and any other small animals, including small fishes, living on the riverbed. It finds its food with the aid of whiskerlike feelers on the underside of its flattened head.

Because of these differences the bony fishes are often divided into Palaeopterygii, or "archaic" fishes, with a partly cartilaginous skeleton, and Neopterygii, or "modern" fishes, with a wholly bony skeleton. The former include the bichirs, sturgeons and paddlefishes.

The eleven species of bichirs live in African rivers. Up to three feet long, they have long bodies and along the mid-line of the back is a series of up to twenty finlets, each made up of a single spine from which spring the fin-rays. Each finlet, when erected, looks like a small flag. The scales are rhombic in shape and composed of an enamel-like substance called ganoin. The newly hatched bichir has feathery external gills. The adults, in addition to breathing by gills, come to the surface to gulp air, and they can survive many hours out of water.

The two dozen species of sturgeon are found in rivers in the north temperate region. They are sharklike in appearance, and this resemblance is heightened by the turned-up tail. The body is scaleless except for five rows of large scales running from head to tail. The head is flattened, almost spadelike, and on the flattened underside are four long fleshy barbels which can detect small animals on or in the river-bed. A protrusible mouth is then pushed out to suck them in, for food. The female may bear up to 5 million eggs, which form the caviar of the gourmet. The different species vary much in maximum size. In North America, for example, the white sturgeon may reach 1,800 pounds, comparable with the larger Russian sturgeon, whereas the lake sturgeon may be only 300 pounds, while the shovelnose, with a maximum length of three feet, weighs only six pounds.

There are only two species of paddlefish, one in the Yangtze River and one in the Mississippi, their maximum lengths being twenty and six feet, respectively. Very sharklike, these fishes have an enormous gape when feeding and a long paddle-like rostrum, which has no known function, projecting in front of the head.

The bowfin, of the eastern United States, is another primitive fish, with heavily armoured head and the body covered with large cycloid scales. Named for its single bow-shaped dorsal fin, this single species is the sole survivor of a family which had its heyday in the geological past. Its jaws are armed with strong teeth, and it feeds voraciously on

An inhabitant of the Mississippi basin and adjacent regions to the east and north, this longnosed **garfish,** or **gar-pike,** grows to a length of nearly five feet. Its body is covered with diamond-shaped scales that make it look like what it is: a survivor from the past. Fossils almost identical to living gars have been found in rocks 50 million years old.

any small animals, including other fishes. This makes it unpopular with fishermen especially as its flesh is not well liked. The male is smaller than the female, and has a black spot bordered with white near the base of the tail fin. He builds a nest among weeds and guards the eggs, and also the young until they are a few weeks old.

The gars or gar-pikes, of North America, are long-bodied, with long slender jaws two or three times the length of the head. They also are primitive, and one peculiar feature is that the vertebrae have ball-and-socket joints, like those of reptiles. The largest, the giant tropical gar of Mexico, is up to ten feet long. The body of a gar is covered with stout diamond-shaped scales of ganoin, another feature of primitive fish. A further peculiarity of the gar-pike is its habit of remaining almost motionless, as if suspended in mid-water, but moving at great speed when a prey fish swims near, taking its prey with a sideways slash of the jaws armed with needle-sharp teeth.

Salmon and Trout

THE NEXT FAMILY (Salmonidae) in systematic order is that which includes the salmon and trout, probably the best known of all fresh-water fishes, and popular as sport fish as well as important commercially. All are indigenous to the temperate and cold waters in the Northern Hemisphere but, as the eggs can be easily transported, salmon and trout have been successfully introduced into suitable areas in the Southern Hemisphere, notably in New Zealand, but also in places such as the upland rivers of Kenya.

There is as much variation in the hues of the various species as there is in their life histories. But all members of the family are distinguishable by the small, fleshy adipose fin on the dorsal surface opposite the anal fin.

Typically salmon are anadromous, migrating from the sea to spawn in rivers, while most trout remain all their lives in fresh water. In

(top left)
Sharklike in appearance, the **sturgeon** has five rows of large scales running from head to tail. Apart from these, however, its body is scaleless. Its spadelike head has four long, fleshy barbels that can detect the small riverbed creatures that make up its diet.

(top right)
Salmon leave the sea to spawn in rivers, sometimes overcoming fantastic obstacles to do so. When she is about to lay her eggs, the female scrapes a hole in the gravel on the river bottom and deposits her eggs in it. The male releases his milt over them and then the female covers them with sand to keep them safe.

(top left)
Most **trout** stay in fresh water. Like the salmon, they are native to temperate and cold-water areas of the northern hemisphere. When first hatched, the baby trout is very helpless and is nourished only through the yolk sac that is still attached to it. Later the young fish takes food through its mouth, in the form of single-celled plankton.

(top right)
Although there is wide disagreement among authorities, most would agree that there are nearly two dozen species of salmon and trout. All have at least one trait in common, a small, fatty fin on the dorsal surface, near the tail. Pictured here is the **rainbow trout.**

both salmon and trout the female scrapes a trough in the gravel of the river-bed, and lays her eggs in it. Simultaneously, the male, which has remained near her all the time, releases his milt over the eggs. The female then covers the eggs with sand for protection. This process is repeated until the female has laid all her eggs. After spawning, salmon usually die; trout, however, may spawn for a number of years.

The eggs hatch between nineteen and eighty days after laying, depending upon the temperature of the water. The young salmon may then migrate to the sea or remain in their streams for up to four years, according to species and prevailing conditions.

Much has been written about the ability of salmon to return "unerringly" to spawn in the river in which they themselves were spawned. But not all salmon manage this correctly, and it was at one time thought that those that do so rely on their sense of smell to find the parent stream. The subject is, however, still wide open for research. In recent years it has been suggested that the returning salmon use celestial navigation to guide them to the vicinity of the river mouth where they first entered the sea.

It is impossible to say how many species of Salmonidae there are, because their classification is a matter of opinion. For example, it was once thought that there were ten species of trout and one species of salmon in the British Isles. This was later reduced to three: the salmon, sea trout and river trout; some authorities go so far as to regard *all* trout as members of a single species. If we disregard extreme opinion we can say that there are nearly two dozen species of salmon and trout, and to these must be added an ill-defined number of species of char, as well as whitefish and grayling, to complete the family.

The Atlantic salmon, Salmo salar, is found in rivers running into the Atlantic and adjacent seas such as the Baltic, from the Bay of Biscay to Novaya Zemlya, in the rivers of Iceland, off the southern tip of Greenland, and along the Atlantic coast of North America, from

(left)
Often included with the salmon, the **grayling** has larger scales, a smaller mouth, and is generally smaller than either the trout or salmon. This popular sport fish is found in fresh water on both sides of the Atlantic.

(below)
Typically, **Atlantic salmon** feed in the sea and return up the rivers to spawn, but there are some land-locked populations of these salmon in lakes as well. They sometimes rival the king salmon of the Pacific coast in size and weight.

Hudson Strait to the New England states. On the eastern side of the Atlantic, the British Isles account for a larger share of the annual catch of salmon than all the rest of Europe combined.

In North America the important catches are on the Pacific coast where the rivers from Alaska to California contain such species as the chinook or king salmon, *Oncorhynchus tschawytscha,* the silver salmon or coho, *O. kisutch,* and the red salmon or sockeye, *O. nerka.* These, with the dog or chum salmon, *O. keta,* and the humpback or pink salmon, *O. gorbuscha,* yield approximately 500 million pounds of commercial fish a year, in canned, fresh, frozen or smoked salmon, as compared with a much smaller yield of Atlantic salmon for Europe, including the British Isles. This is not the total catch of *Oncorhynchus* because salmon of this genus inhabit the rivers along the Pacific coast of Asia, from the Bering Sea to Korea, including Japan.

Not all salmonids are river fish and migratory. *Salmo carpio* is found only in Lake Garda, in Italy. The lake or mackinaw trout, *Salvelinus namaycush,* used to support a valuable commercial fishery in the Great Lakes until the invasion by the sea lamprey virtually wiped out the fishery. In addition there are the many species of char (*Salvelinus*) typical of mountain lakes in Europe.

The chinook or king salmon grows to five feet in length and 100 pounds in weight, dimensions that are rivalled by the largest Atlantic salmon. These exceed by a fair margin the other large salmonids, such as the dog or chum salmon (three feet, thirty pounds), silver or coho salmon (two and one-half feet, twenty-six and one-half pounds) red or sockeye salmon (two and one-half feet, fifteen and one-half pounds), and the humpback or pink salmon (two feet, six pounds).

The whitefish (*Coregonus*) and grayling (*Thymallus*), each in its separate family, are very similar to the salmon and trout. Like them they are found in temperate waters of the Northern Hemisphere, and have an adipose dorsal fin, opposite the anal fin. The main differences lie in the larger scales, smaller mouths, and generally smaller size of the whitefish and grayling. Four pounds is the maximum for both types, as against eleven pounds for the smallest species of trout. Despite this, both are popular sport fish and the whitefish is important commercially.

The Arapaima

BY CONTRAST WITH THE SALMONIDAE, the Galaxidae are found only in the Southern Hemisphere: in New Zealand, Australia, South Africa and the southernmost part of South America. The distribution of these fishes is cited as evidence that all these lands were once part of a large southern continent. Another interesting feature is that these fishes are found in areas very similar to those in which trout are found in the Northern Hemisphere.

There are about thirty-six species of galaxids, and all are elongate and scaleless, with a single dorsal and a single anal fin, situated just in front of the tail. With the exception of the giant galaxid of New Zealand, which averages twelve inches in length, these fishes are all small, four to six inches being their maximum length.

One species, the New Zealand brown mudfish, has no ventral fin and, like the South American and African lungfishes, can survive for several weeks in the mud of dried-up lakes and rivers.

Although rivalled, and possibly exceeded, in size by the South American catfish, it is generally held that the arapaima, a member of the family of the Osteoglossidae (bony-tongued fishes), is the largest completely fresh-water fish. It is said to reach a length of fifteen feet, but not all the five species in this family reach such a size. All, however, are similar in having large prominent scales, big eyes and a head covered with bony plates. The dorsal and anal fins are set so far back on the body that they appear continuous with the tail.

Olive green, becoming reddish towards the tail, which is scarlet, the arapaima, despite its size and average weight of 200 pounds, can move both fast and gracefully. It has a large air bladder, used as a lung, which opens directly into the throat.

The arapaima and the smaller related African species both build nests in the breeding season. The arapaima makes a nest about twenty inches in diameter and six inches deep, by scraping a hollow in the sandy river-bed with its fins; the same nest may continue to be used for several years. The African fish, however, makes a much more elaborate nest: it is often four feet in diameter and its walls, made of the vegetation removed from the centre, may be several inches thick. Of the remaining three species in the group, one, the arawana, is found in South America, and the others in Malaya and Australia. All three have fleshy chin barbels and are mouth-brooders, incubating their eggs in the mouth or throat.

The female **Egyptian mouth-brooder** takes her eggs into her mouth immediately after spawning. The young hatching from them return to her mouth in moments of danger, and they also take shelter there during the night. For a week after hatching, this procedure continues.

The Butterfly Fish and the Mooneye

THE BUTTERFLY FISH OF WEST AFRICA (family Pantodontidae) seems incongruous as a relative of the arapaima, for it never exceeds five inches in length. Little is known about this fish, which swims just below the surface, and can make leaps of six feet or more out of the water. The large pectoral fins may enable it to glide when making these leaps, but despite the fact that it is often called a flying fish it does not fly in the true sense. Another peculiarity is that the pelvic fins are extended into long slender rays unconnected with each other by any membrane.

With its large, silvery scales, **chalceus** looks something like a miniature tarpon, a much larger game fish. This species may grow to twelve inches and is found in the Guianas, Brazil and Venezuela.

The three herring-like species of the mooneye (Hiodontidae) family are confined to the northern, central and eastern parts of North America. Silvery and with a large eye, the mooneye or toothed herring reaches a maximum of seventeen inches and two and one-half pounds in weight. Found only in clear water, it is considered a good sport fish but is not a food fish. A second species, the goldeneye, is slightly larger and is similar to the mooneye in appearance, except that it is darker on the dorsal surface and has a sharp ridge on the belly in front of the ventral fins. The goldeneye can tolerate muddy water.

Featherback Fishes

THE CHILD WHO DECLARED, as a result of watching them in an aquarium, that fishes swim by waggling their tails was not far wrong. In most fishes locomotion is by sinuous movements of the body aided by the broad surfaces of the tail fin. There are, however, occasional exceptions.

Featherback fishes use the slender dorsal fin as a rudder, and propulsion is mainly provided by rippling movements of the anal fin which extends along the undersurface of the body, from just behind the head to the tail. Featherbacks, named for the elegant movements of the dorsal fin, are found in West Africa, and from India, through South-east Asia, to Australia. The largest of the four species is found in India and South-east Asia, and may reach three feet in length, the other species being slightly smaller. All are valued as food, and in Thailand posts are driven into the ponds to provide artificial spawning sites. Around these posts the female lays from five to ten thousand eggs, which are closely guarded by the male during the five- to six-day incubation period.

Electrical Fish from Africa

THERE ARE TWO WAYS OF REMEMBERING that fishes of the next family, Mormyridae, are exclusively African. The first is by comparing the tendency in some members towards a prominent lower lip

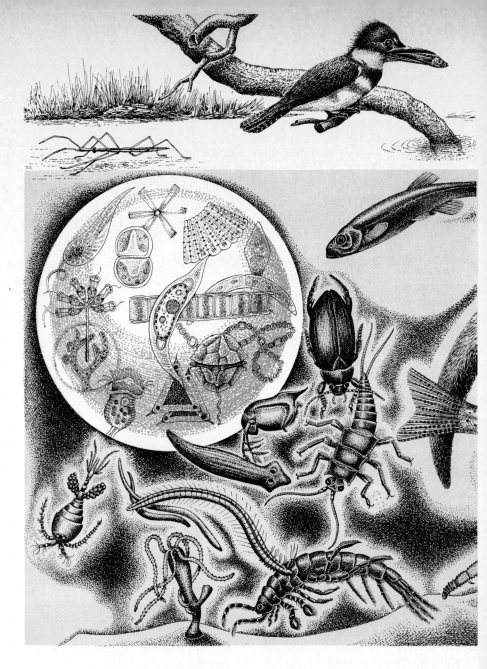

A **fresh-water food chain** starts with diatoms, algae and other microscopic life (shown, greatly magnified, in the circle). These are eaten by water fleas, water striders, nymphs, beetles and worms. Larger animals, in turn, eat these and are eaten by small fish. Still larger fish and the kingfisher bird prey on the small fish; and at the top of this chain is the otter, which can catch and eat the biggest fish.

recalling the enlarged lower lip once favored by an African tribe, the Ubangi. The other is the frequency with which representations of one mormyrid, *Mormyrus caballus*, from the Upper Nile, are found on Egyptian antiquities.

There is much variation within the one hundred and ten species. Typical of all is the unusually narrow caudal peduncle, the part of the tail between the body and the tail fin. In addition, the single dorsal fin and the single anal fin are set opposite each other, well back on the body, and the tail fin is deeply forked. Although some species may reach a length of five feet, most of them are no more than six inches long.

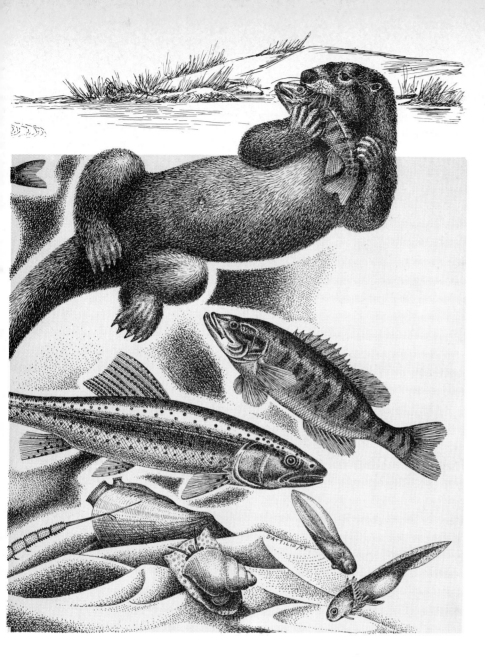

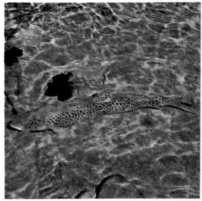

Although the **brown trout** is native to Europe, it has been widely introduced into North America. As a game fish it is swift and agile, and to capture it requires considerable skill. In large lakes, with abundant food, the brown trout will grow up to fifty pounds.

Many of the species can be easily recognized by the unusual developments of the mouth and snout. Several have very elongated snouts, curved and inflexible, with the small mouth situated at the end. In others, only the flexible lower lip is elongated; yet other species have rounded noses without extensions, but with the mouth set well back on the ventral surface of the head. Mormyrids are bottom feeders, and the elongated head parts are used in searching in the mud for worms, insect larvae and small invertebrates.

Another interesting feature of this family is that all species emit electrical impulses into the water, from muscle tissue which has become modified to form electrical organs. This ability enables them to find

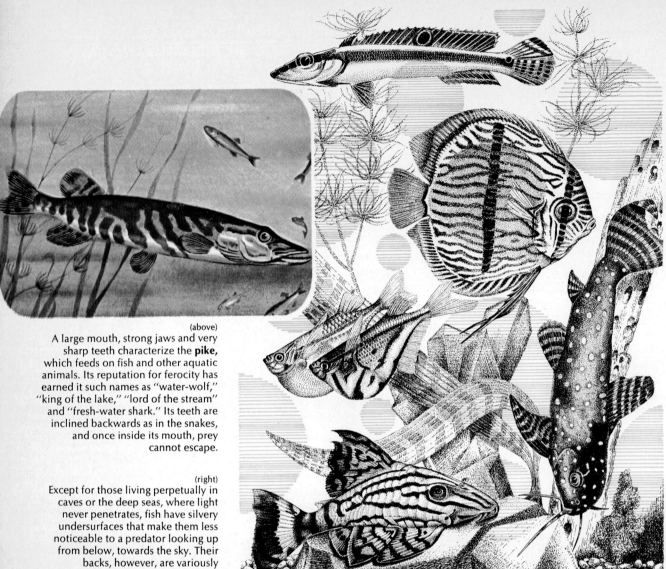

(above)
A large mouth, strong jaws and very sharp teeth characterize the **pike,** which feeds on fish and other aquatic animals. Its reputation for ferocity has earned it such names as "water-wolf," "king of the lake," "lord of the stream" and "fresh-water shark." Its teeth are inclined backwards as in the snakes, and once inside its mouth, prey cannot escape.

(right)
Except for those living perpetually in caves or the deep seas, where light never penetrates, fish have silvery undersurfaces that make them less noticeable to a predator looking up from below, towards the sky. Their backs, however, are variously patterned, and this makes them hard to distinguish from above.

food and to avoid obstacles and enemies in the muddy waters in which they live, because any object coming into the electrical field surrounding their bodies is immediately pinpointed.

One species, *Gymnarchus niloticus,* is capable of even more refined electrical activity. The impulses constitute a true radar, and the fish can swim backwards as well as forwards without colliding with any obstacles, in muddy water or in total darkness. For a long time *Gymnarchus* was classified separately, as it looked so different from other mormyrids, having lost its ventral, anal and caudal fins and developed instead a dorsal fin running almost the entire length of its eel-like body. This fish also differs from other members of the family in building a floating nest. The nest is made of vegetation, and two of its sides and one end are projected above the water-line; the other end, which is below water, serves as the entrance. In this nest are laid a thousand eggs each nearly half an inch in diameter.

The Pike Family

THE PIKE HAS A WELL-DESERVED REPUTATION for ferocity. It is the wolf of the northern waters—and also the glutton. There are many stories to illustrate this, including one of a pike which seized a salmon as big as itself; the salmon was subdued only after a combat lasting two hours. The pike then began to swallow the salmon head first, and it was three days before it had engulfed the whole body. For a week the pike was swollen and refused to move even when prodded with a long stick.

All members of the pike family have large mouths, strong jaws and very sharp teeth, and are voracious carnivores. Although their food is chiefly fish they will also take frogs and water birds and other aquatic animals. The pike is the most widely-spread species from North America, from about latitude 40° N northwards, across Europe to Asia. The record weight is seventy-two pounds, and the length nearly five feet.

Despite their size and apparent toughness, however, pike are very susceptible to slight changes in environment, which is the probable reason why they have been known to disappear from areas where they were once common.

The pike and its close relatives, the pickerels and the muskellunge, of North America, are spring spawners, laying their eggs indiscriminately in areas of shallow weedy water.

The muskellunge, of the region of the Great Lakes, is even larger than the pike, with a record weight of 102 pounds. The chain pickerel, ranging from Nova Scotia to Texas, reaches a length of two feet, but the grass pickerel, of the eastern United States, seldom exceeds one foot. All are similar in appearance, with the heavy head and the dorsal and anal fins set far back on the body.

Mud Minnows and Blackfish

APART FROM THE FACT that they have rounded rather than shovel-shaped snouts, the North American mud minnows (family Umbridae) are very similar in appearance to the pikes to which they are related. They are, however, smaller; the largest of the three species, the central mud minnow, reaches a maximum length of six inches, and the average is only about two inches. These fishes are aptly named for, with their tails, they readily dig themselves into the mud, to hide —or to "laze away" the summer. This is particularly interesting as they

Able to stay out of the water for long periods, the **mudskipper** can travel over the mud using its front fins as legs. While on land it feeds on insects and may even climb trees. It lives on the muddy shores of Southeast Asia and is occasionally found inland in fresh water.

have no lungs, and yet are able to live in water with a very low oxygen content, and can also survive for days buried in the mud. They breed in the early spring, and with its approach the anal fin of the male central mud minnow develops a blue-green iridescence. The number of eggs laid by the female each season is quite variable, and may be anything from 200 to 1,500.

Farther north, the Alaska blackfish is distributed across the most northerly parts of North America, Asia and Europe; it is the Arctic equivalent of the mud minnow but somewhat larger, reaching a maximum length of eight inches.

There are many stories of the blackfish's ability to survive great extremes of cold, even to the point of being frozen within a solid block of ice. This has not been definitely proved, and tests suggest it is only able to survive such freezing if no ice crystals form within the tissue of the body itself.

Piranhas and Tiger Fish

ALTHOUGH THE CHARACINS form a very large family (Characidae), with much variety of form and size, their distribution is limited to Central and South America and to tropical Africa.

Probably the best-known members of the family are the four species of South American piranhas, notorious for their great ferocity in attacking man as well as other animals. The stories are often exaggerated; nevertheless, these fish have very many sharp teeth in their strong jaws, and, hunting in schools, can reduce their prey to a bare skeleton in a surprisingly short time. It is on the record that a hundred-pound capybara was stripped of all flesh within a minute. Even when caught and apparently dead the fish is liable to snap its jaws at anything that touches it, and can easily slash a finger or toe.

(above)
Named after the Brazilian town of Serpa, on the Amazon, the **red serpae** is one of the many species of characins. It was imported into Europe in 1931, and two years later aquarists introduced it in the United States. Under overhead, artificial light, its hues can be seen to best advantage.

(right)
The **firemouth** is named for its coloring and not its temperament. Native to Guatemala and Yucatan, this fish is colored brick-red about the throat and lower jaw, but most of its body is bluish-grey with a purplish sheen.

The tiger fish of the Congo, also, has been held responsible for attacks on humans. Whether this is true or not, this troutlike fish, with a maximum weight of 125 pounds, is very dangerous to handle when landed, because it can inflict serious wounds with its large conical tearing teeth.

By contrast with these, the closely related silver dollar fish, usually four to six inches, at most two feet long, is mainly herbivorous and is very popular with those who keep tropical fish.

Flying Fish

AMONG THE MANY CHARACINS there is also diversity in habits. Several species, known as "tailstanders", swim in a vertical position with the head upwards: others, known as "headstanders", swim head-down. They generally have the mouth at the tip of the snout, which enables them to scrape algae from water plants and rocks. With the mouth in this position these fishes can, and sometimes do, feed on their backs.

Upwards of sixty species of this popular family of characins are kept in aquaria, including the several species of tetras. One of these is the only true flying fish. Found from Panama south to the mouth of the River Plate, the flying characins or flying hatchet fishes are the only fishes that can actually propel themselves through the air by beating their fins like wings, whereas other "flying fish" merely glide through the air. These small, insect-feeding fish use the powers of flight, produced by the action of unusually large pectoral muscles on greatly developed pectoral fins, to escape from enemies.

When spawning most characins lay their eggs indiscriminately among the water plants and they show no parental care towards either the eggs or young. A few species make seasonal migrations to the headwaters of their rivers or streams to breed.

One species, *Copeina arnoldi,* has very unusual breeding behavior. The species is better known to aquarists as *Pyrrulina filamentosa.* The male and female, with fins locked together, leap out of the water, landing on a leaf or rock at the edge of a stream, where they cling by fin suction for about ten seconds. Between six and twelve eggs are laid, and the pair then fall back into the water. This is repeated at the same spot until all the eggs have been laid and form a gelatinous mass about two inches in diameter. Then, until the eggs hatch, in about three days, the male prevents them from drying up by splashing water over them with his tail every ten to fifteen minutes. It seems that when the eggs hatch, the male does not guard the young.

A particularly interesting feature of this family is that many of its members closely resemble species in other groups to which they are unrelated. For example, the blind Mexican cave fish, or blind characin, looks very similar to the blind African barbel; other species look like trout, and one species resembles superficially the salt-water herring.

(top)
A fish with an evil reputation, the **piranha** is one of several related species from Brazil. Although their normal diet is fish, piranhas have reportedly attacked other animals in the shoals, chopping at the flesh of alligators or capybaras (large South American rodents) with their stout teeth.

(above)
Most species of characin show no parental interest in the eggs or young. The male of one species, however, is particularly attentive, splashing the eggs with water every ten or fifteen minutes to keep them moist. It is known, appropriately, as the spraying characin. The fish pictured here is the tiny **red-eyed characin,** which lives in the streams of tropical West Africa.

The "Electric Eel"

DESPITE THEIR APPEARANCE and the fact that some are termed "eel", the gymnotid fishes are unrelated to eels. In fact they are closely related to the characins.

In appearance the *Gymnotidae* are identifiable by their cylindrical ribbon-like bodies, small eyes, the slender pointed tail that may or may not have a fin. There is no true dorsal fin with fin rays, and the anal fin, on the undersurface, may extend for three-quarters to four-fifths of the fish's length. This fin enables the fish to move up or down, forward or backward, with equal ease. In the knifefishes, this fin extends into a long mobile tail with which they are able to feel their way backward into rock crevices.

Gymnotids are found only in South and Central America, from Guatemala to Paraguay and Argentina. Relatively little is known of their life histories, but it is now fairly certain that most of the species are able to emit electrical impulses onto the surrounding water to enable them to find food and avoid obstacles and enemies. Some gymnotids are superficially remarkably like the African *Gymnarchus* (family Mormyridae), but whereas this species gives out a continuous electric discharge, the gymnotids give out intermittent impulses.

The electric eel has this ability to the greatest degree, four-fifths of its long, slender body being taken up by the electrical organs, which are capable of producing 600 volts of electricity. However, the shock from this may not be as great as at first seems likely, for the amperage of the discharge is low. There are three types of battery in this fish. The largest is used defensively and for paralyzing prey; of the other two, one is a sonar battery and the other one is thought to be used in conjunction with the main battery. The sonar battery is used for location of food, for as the fish becomes older, the eyes become cloudy, and presumably its sight deteriorates. Apart from two small stabilizing pectoral fins, the only fin the electric eel has is the long anal fin, which runs from the vent to the tail tip.

The electric eel has an unusual method of respiration. It breathes air, and every fifteen minutes comes to the surface for a fresh supply. It will drown if unable to do this. It has no lungs and hardly uses its gills. Instead, there are patches of tissue within the mouth very well supplied with blood vessels which enable it to absorb oxygen directly from the air.

This bullhead of Europe and Asia is called the **miller's thumb,** possibly because its shape recalls the spoon-shaped thumb of the old-time miller, acquired through using his thumb to test flour. Also known as the slimy sculpin, it is an inhabitant of shallow streams.

Gyrinocheilid and Hillstream Fishes

IN THAILAND AND THE SURROUNDING REGION, there is an unusual fish that was classified as a loach for many years. Later it was classified as a minnow, and finally was put into a completely separate family of its own. This is the small family of gyrinocheilid fishes, of about ten inches average length, characterized by their almost unique method of respiration. The external gill openings are divided into an upper and a lower section; water enters the upper section by means of a special inhalant channel, passes across the gills to the pharynx, returns over the gills and out through the lower section of the gill openings. The respiratory rate is high, 230 to 240 times a minute in a five-inch fish. These fishes live in fast-flowing mountain streams, and because they do not use their mouths for breathing they are able to browse continuously the algae growing on the rocks; they can also hold on to rocks or other protuberances, to prevent themselves from getting swept away by the swift current.

The members of this herbivorous family are easily recognizable by the large fleshy lips surrounding the forward part of the jaw.

Closely related, and in many ways similar to the loaches, are the hillstream fishes (family Homalopteridae) of south and east Asia and the islands of the Indo-Australian archipelago. They are well adapted to their habitat of swift flowing mountain streams. Their heads are rounded, their bodies streamlined, and on the undersurface of the fish a large, cup-shaped sucking disk has been developed from the pectoral and pelvic fins. Pumping action of the free portions of the pectoral fins draws water away from underneath the sucker and creates a vacuum which enables the fish to remain attached to any rock or other protuberance.

Other features of the hillstream fishes are: very small cycloid scales, pharyngeal teeth, at least three pairs of mouth barbels, small dorsal and anal fins, and small gill openings often fairly high up on the sides of the body.

In many species of this group, breathing is an intermittent process; for a while respiration is regular, then it stops, for varying lengths of time. Most of the species that breathe in this manner have an enlarged pharynx and gill cavities which serve as water reservoirs; these reduce the usable part of the external gill openings to the upper part only.

Suckers and Loaches

THE SUCKERS (FAMILY CATOSTOMIDAE) are a group which is closely related to the carps and minnows. They are mainly bottom-grubbers, and apart from a few Asian species, they are found chiefly in America. In many ways similar to the minnows in appearance, one big difference is that their very protrusible mouth is on the underside of the head and is surrounded by thick fleshy lips. The humpback sucker of the Colorado River has developed an inverted boatlike keel along the back. Water flowing over the fish is thus caused to assist the fish in maintaining its position without effort.

The small elongated loaches (family Cobitidae) have from six to twelve barbels around the mouth, small scales and throat teeth instead

Like many other Old World fishes, the **tinsel barb** is characterized by the tactile barbels around its mouth. These are organs of touch, and they are used by this bottom-feeder in searching the bed of the river or lake for food. It has a reputation as a glutton.

(top left)
Because it absorbs oxygen by swallowing air, the **loach** can live in water with low oxygen content. It has six to twelve barbels around its mouth.

(top right)
Often used as bait, the common **minnows** of streams and brooks are the prey of fish-eating birds and of larger fishes.

(above, left)
An important fish in low-protein areas of the world, the **common carp** is now found in most temperate regions. This picture shows its skeleton.

(above, right)
The **golden tench,** a bottom-dwelling minnow, may weigh as much as seventeen pounds.

of teeth in the jaws. A few species have a movable spine in front of or below each eye; its function is still unknown. Loaches have an unusual method of respiration. They swallow air and absorb the oxygen from it as it passes through the digestive system; because of this they can live in water with a very low oxygen content.

The spotted weatherfish, or spined loach, is tolerant of an unusually wide range of temperatures. It is equally comfortable in waters of 40° and those of 80° Fahrenheit. The European weatherfish, moreover, is particularly sensitive to fluctuations in barometric pressure, as shown by its increased activity before a storm. This activity consists of disturbed and uncomfortable movements.

Minnows and Carps

ONE OF THE LARGEST GROUPS of bony fishes are the cyprinids. The family Cyprinidae, which probably originated in southern Asia, and has since spread to northern Asia, Europe and North America, includes the minnows and carps.

In a family with at least 1,200 species there is naturally much variety. The majority of the fishes are small, less than eighteen inches long, but some, such as the Indian mahseer, reach a length of nine feet and have scales the size of the palm of one's hand. But whatever their size, all have cycloid scales and lack the adipose fin.

While the majority are omnivorous, some cyprinids are lethargic bottom-dwelling herbivores and others are fiercely carnivorous. All carps and minnows have toothless jaws but have strong throat teeth. Mouth barbels are present in a few species.

One of the most unusual North American species is the stone-roller which, as its name suggests, rolls stones over to eat the algae growing underneath. In the breeding season the males become reddish and develop tubercles on the upper surface of the body. They also hollow out cup-shaped nests in the stream bed by flicking the gravel away with sideways movements of the head.

One of the most common and widely distributed of European and Asian minnows is the golden tench. This bottom-dwelling species has two mouth barbels which may help it find its food at the bottom of muddy ponds. Although eight pounds is generally regarded as large for this fish, some have been recorded as weighing seventeen pounds.

Most of this group of fishes just lay their eggs at random among the water plants, but a few have more unusual breeding habits. The stone-roller is one example; and another is the bitterling, of Central Europe. With each breeding season, the female bitterling develops a long ovipositor which she inserts into the mantle cavity of fresh-water mussels—and there lays her eggs. These hatch within the shellfish, apparently causing it no inconvenience. (At the same time the mussel expels its own larvae which cling to the bitterling and are carried away. This assists in dispersing the mussels.)

(bottom left)
Originally from around the Black and Caspian seas, the hardy and adaptable **carp** is an easy fish to cultivate. It is raised for food in hatcheries in many parts of the world, sometimes escaping and establishing itself successfully in lakes and ponds.

(bottom right)
Because the **wild goldfish,** like the related carp, is easily bred in captivity, it has been the subject of many hybridization experiments. From this Asiatic species alone have come some spectacular varieties, much prized by aquarists.

Using her ovipositor, which becomes long during the breeding season, the female **bitterling** lays her eggs between the valves of a swan mussel. At the same time, the mussel larvae are released, attach themselves to the bitterling and are carried away. Later they drop off, thus helping the mussels to disperse. This exchange, it seems, causes no inconvenience to either party.

The **spotted sucker catfish** of South America grazes algae that grow in films on stones and leaves. It rests hanging vertically from leaves, holding on by its sucking mouth.

As varied as they are numerous, **catfishes** sometimes have unusual properties and habits. One African species can send out an electric discharge of a hundred volts; some South American species have whiskers as long as their bodies; and one catfish in Thailand makes croaking noises, both in and out of water. There are parasitic catfishes, transparent catfishes, catfishes with poison glands, and many others besides. Out of eleven families, nine live in fresh water.

The carp is one of the larger members of this family. Although it originated around the Black and Caspian seas, it is a hardy fish which has survived introduction into new areas, and it is now found in temperate regions throughout most of the world. An easy fish to cultivate, it is important in those parts of the world where there is a scarcity of cheap, high-protein food.

Many cyprinid fishes are popular with aquarists, for they breed easily in captivity, and so lend themselves to breeding and hybridization experiments. From the carp and wild goldfish alone, many spectacular varieties have been developed, while the barbels of the Old World make attractive additions to any collection of tropical fish. The many species of *Rasbora* are also well liked by aquarists.

Catfishes

CATFISHES ARE FOUND in both fresh and salt water. The numerous species, although assigned to several families, are readily recognizable by the whisker-like barbels around the mouth. All are scaleless, but some have a bony, platelike armor, so we speak of armored and naked catfishes, the most heavily armored being the six species of barbel catfish of South America with the armor decorated with bumps and hooks.

Most catfishes are bottom-dwellers. Many have the mouth on the underside of the head, with bi-lobed or spoon-shaped teeth well adapted for scraping small plants from the rocks. They usually rest in a vertical position, hanging on to plants with the aid of the pelvic fins and a mouth disk.

The South American banjo catfish are included among the naked catfishes, although their bony heads give the impression of armor. They are nocturnal, hiding by day among the water plants. They have a tail at least three times as long as the head and body.

The **channel catfish** grows to a length of four feet and a weight of fifty-seven pounds. In the central United States it is used as a food fish. The young have black spots on the flanks, but with age the body grows darker and the spots become masked.

One species from the Guianas has an unusual method of incubating. In the breeding season the female develops spongy tentacles on its belly, to which the eggs remain attached until they hatch.

The clarid catfishes, found from Africa to the East Indies, have auxiliary respiratory organs in a pocket which extends up and backwards from the gill cavity, and these enable them to survive for some time out of water.

The closely-related West African eelcats have very long dorsal and anal fins continuous with the tail fin, and the body is hardly thicker than a pencil, although the fish may be twelve inches in length.

The European wels belongs to a family (the Siluridae) of catfishes ranging from Europe and Africa to Indonesia, with unusually long anal fins. These are their chief means of locomotion. One of the largest of all catfish, it is said to reach a length of thirteen feet, and a weight of 650 pounds. By contrast the transparent glass catfish, of the same family, has a maximum length of three inches. Some South American catfishes have whiskers as long as the body. One of the most extraordinary catfishes is the croaking catfish of Thailand. Whether in or out of water it emits loud croaking noises.

The small slender South American parasitic catfishes have recurved spines with which they can hook themselves on to anything they meet. Not all are parasitic, but those that are eat the gill filaments and drink the blood of their hosts.

The madtoms, small catfishes up to five inches long, have poison glands associated with their pectoral spines, and can cause dangerous wounds.

One tropical African group of catfishes, aptly termed "upside-down catfish", can swim with equal ease either way up! They, too, make grunting sounds—by rotating the dorsal and pectoral spines in their sockets.

Throughout tropical central Africa to the Nile valley is found the electric catfish, a pugnacious fish, capable of emitting electric discharges of 100 volts. The electric cells are situated in the fatty layer just under

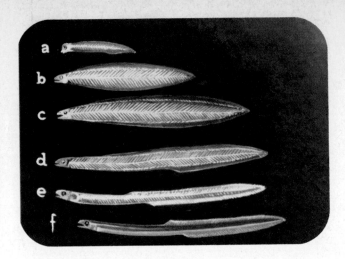

Eels are fresh-water fish until they are about to spawn. Then they migrate to the sea. After laying their eggs, they die, leaving the larvae to travel back to fresh waters; this journey back to the coast takes one year for the young of the American eel, and nearly three years for those of the European eel.

Stages in the **development of the eel** are illustrated in this drawing. The flat, leaflike, colorless larvae (a, b) drift back to the coasts. Then they begin to change, becoming more cylindrical (c, d), but still lacking color. As the whitish, threadlike creatures start up the rivers, color finally appears (e, f); these are the elvers, or young eels.

the skin. This fish was well known to the ancient Egyptians, who depicted it on their tombs.

Fresh-Water Eels

MANY FISHES ARE CALLED EELS, and together they form the order Apodes, but there is only one family represented in fresh waters. That is the family Anguillidae, which includes the European and the American eel, as well as species found in the river systems and off-shore islands of South-east Asia, parts of Australia, and New Zealand. All are peculiar in being the only catadromous fishes; they spend their post-larval and adult lives in rivers and lakes and migrating to the sea to spawn. After spawning they die, and the larvae hatching from the eggs make the journey to fresh waters.

For centuries the European eel remained a mystery fish not only because the larvae were unknown, but because no sexually mature eel had ever been found. So arose many myths: that eels rubbed their skin off on rocks and these fragments developed into young eels; that horsehairs falling in water turned into eels; and that eels mated with serpents. The truth, so far as the European and American eels are concerned, began to be revealed in the early years of this century. Now it is well known that both species leave the rivers when fully grown and journey to a point in the Sargasso Sea, south of Bermuda, where they spawn in deep water.

The larvae, leaf-shaped and about three inches long, known as leptocephali, return to the mouths of the rivers, where they change into elvers or young eels, of about the same length. Leptocephali of the American eel take a year, those of the European eel take nearly three years, to reach the coast. The males remain in fresh waters near the coast, the females migrate up the rivers and into the lakes, and even move across land to do this.

This beautiful **Siamese fighting fish** is the result of centuries of selective breeding. Its wild relatives are drab, two inches long and have small fins. In Thailand the aggressive males are matched against each other in contests.

Eels are long, with cylindrical bodies. They lack pelvic fins, and their dorsal and anal fins are continuous with the tail fin. Their swimbladder opens by a duct into the throat. Their scales are vestigial or altogether absent.

Flying Fishes, Needlefishes and Half-Beaks

ANOTHER GROUP OF FISHES has most of its members living in the sea. This is the group that includes the flying fishes, needlefishes and half-beaks. But aquarists will know there is a fresh-water half-beak, at most about three inches long, which is a famous wrestler. The name indicates that the lower jaw is very long and the upper jaw very short, as if half the "beak" had been removed. Yet the males, famous as fighting fish in Thailand, fight by seizing each other by the jaws and wrestling until one gives up. Another peculiarity of the fresh-water half-beak is that the young are born alive.

Mollies, Guppies and Swordtails

BY CONTRAST, THE NEXT GROUP, the Microcyprini, with numerous species, are almost entirely fresh-water. A few live in brackish, or even salt water, but the overwhelming fresh-water nature of the group is shown by the many species familiar to aquarists: the mollies, the guppies, the swordtails, to name merely three of the best-known.

The first family of Microcyprini are the Amblyopsidae, the blind cave fishes of North America. Included also is the ricefish, a swamp-dweller with functional but very small eyes, and the springfish, also with small eyes. All species find their way about by means of tactile organs in the skin. For the most part their breeding habits are unknown but the females of one species are known to incubate their eggs in their gill cavities—presumably laid there by a long ovipositor.

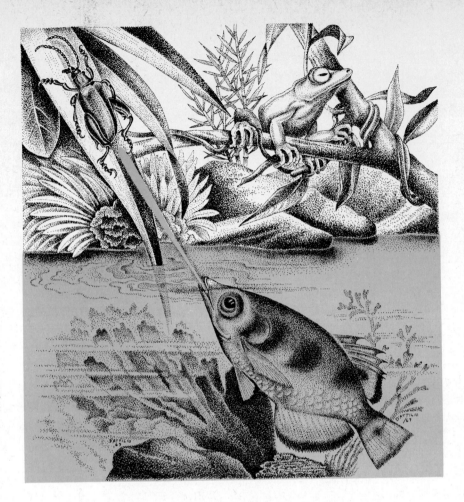

A skillful marksman, the **archer fish** shoots down insects by ejecting drops of water at them from its mouth. Once it was thought that the fish was able to allow for a slanting position in taking aim, but recent research suggests that it positions itself as directly under the target as possible.

The next family is that of the egg-laying topminnows or killies (Cyprinodontidae), also known as annual fishes. Of the 200 known species the majority are found in America and Africa, with some in southern Europe and southern Asia. Their habitat is one in which heavy rains alternate with periods of drought. At most a few inches long, they include species like the bluefins, lyretails and pearl fishes. Typically, the annual fishes live only for a year—or at most a few months longer than this. As the shallow waters they inhabit dry up the fishes breed, laying their eggs in the mud, and then they die. The eggs resist desiccation, and with the first rains they hatch and the young fishes grow rapidly. Bacteria in the mud help to soften the toughened coats of the eggs and the fry which emerge feed on the numerous single-celled animals nourished by the decaying bodies of the parent fishes.

Dealers have been quick to exploit this breeding habit; besides being convenient to send eggs in mud or damp peat by mail, the recipient aquarist can have the fun of hatching the eggs by covering them with water.

Guppies are probably the best known of the very numerous viviparous topminnows (family Poeciliidae). In this large group, fertilization is internal, one set of sperm fertilizing several batches of eggs. The male's gonopodium, or intromittent organ, is formed from the anterior rays of the anal fin.

One species, the Amazon molly, exists only as a female population, the males of closely related species being used in the breeding season to maintain the species. Another species has two distinct types of female; those that produce only female young, and the other group which produces both males and females.

Mosquito Fish and Fish with Four Eyes

THERE ARE SEVERAL SPECIES of mosquito fish, so called because they feed chiefly on the larvae and pupae of these insects, and so are important in tropical countries in helping keep down the numbers of mosquitoes.

In British Guiana, Venezuela and Brazil is found an unusual inch-long fish. The male has a very well developed gonopodium, but the young are not born alive; instead each female lays one hard-shelled egg, which develops quickly into a free-swimming young.

In Mexico and Central America live the small family of goodeids. They are related to the poeciliids, but the young are not born alive, the males do not have a very well developed gonopodium, and each batch of sperm can only fertilize one lot of eggs.

The four-eyed fish of tropical America has each eye divided into two distinct parts. As the fish swims just below the surface of the water the upper part of the eye is above the water-line. Not only does the fish have two distinct corneas, one for above and one for underwater vision, but the retinas are also separate. What advantage the fish gains from this is unknown.

(above)
A cichlid well known to aquarists, the **Jack Dempsey,** is a native of South America. It is a good breeder, hardy and responsive to its owners, and has the additional attraction for aquarists of living for ten years or more.

(left)
The **four-eyed fish** of tropical America has each eye divided horizontally into two parts. Its habit is to swim at the surface, feeding on insects. The formation of its eyes enables it to see equally well above and below the surface of the water.

(bottom left)

Mostly green with a yellowish cast and with dark bars on its sides, the European **perch** is easily hidden in the shoals of lakes and sluggish rivers. It preys on smaller fishes. A similar fish in North America is the yellow perch.

(bottom right)

Pike-perches are valued as food fish in Europe and the Soviet Union. Like other perches, they have two spiny dorsal fins.

(below)

Largest of the fresh-water sunfishes, the **largemouth black bass** is native to North America. It is a favorite game fish in the warmer waters of the southern United States, where its weight may reach twenty-five pounds.

These fishes are viviparous, but the external reproductive organs have developed in such a way that some of the fishes are "right-handed", and others are "left-handed", and a left-handed male can mate only with a right-handed female—and vice versa.

Perchlike Fishes

THE TROUTPERCH, OR SANDROLLER (family Percopsidae) is found chiefly in shallow waters in Canada and the northern United States. Generally six inches long, it has an adipose fin, spiny fins and rough ctenoid scales.

The pirateperch (family Aphredoderidae) is unusual in that the vent migrates as the fish grows; in the young fish it is in the usual position, just ahead of the anal fin—but by the time the fish is adult, it occupies a position in the throat, between the gill openings.

Perchlike fishes include many small fishes living in shallow pools and streams. The sunfishes (family Centrarchidae) of North America are so called because they readily respond to sunshine, dispersing and taking shelter among water-plants when the sky is overcast. The North American yellow perch (family Percidae) is an important commercial fish in the Great Lakes. At spawning time the females of this species lay their eggs at night, in long strings which may be up to eighty-one inches long. Walleyes and darters usually lay their eggs at random over the stream or lake beds. A few species of walleye make spawning migrations to small tributary streams, and one of the darters lays its eggs under a rock or in a cave, where the male mounts guard until they are hatched.

The four species of archer fish are found in the Indo-Australian region. Their maximum length is seven and one-half inches, and they can live equally well in fresh, brackish or salt water. All four species have the remarkable ability of ejecting water from their mouths at prey several inches out of the water. To accomplish this the archer fish positions itself to minimize refraction of light and so can hit the prey with a considerable degree of accuracy.

Leaf Fishes and Cichlids

Leaf fishes (family Nandidae) are found in the Amazon and Rio Negro basins in South America. The degree to which a leaf fish simulates a leaf floating in the water is quite remarkable, not only in the shape of its laterally compressed body, and in hue, but also in the way in which it swims with its head at a downward angle. The fish also has a very protrusible mouth and large jaws with which it is able to engulf fish quite half its own size as it drifts by them. When disturbed it is able to move very rapidly.

The six hundred or so species of hardy, aggressive cichlids (family Cichlidae) range from South and Central America, and from Africa to India. The discus, a South American cichlid, is remarkable for the feeding habits of its young. During the first four days after hatching they are attached to the skin of the parent by a short thread having been placed there by the parent using its mouth. They feed on special secretions from mucous cells, and even after they have become free-swimming they continue for a while to feed from the parent's skin.

Many cichlids are mouth-breeders; that is, the male takes an egg into his mouth where it later hatches, and the young will return to his mouth if there is danger. In Africa, more especially, cichlids have formed an important item of diet and one of the mouth-breeders, *Tilapia mossambica*, has been introduced into many parts of the world as a source of food for the local populations. They are prolific breeders and can be easily cultivated in new areas if the competition from indigenous species is not too severe.

Labyrinth Fishes

Labyrinth fishes are small fishes living in South-east Asia and Africa, with special breathing organs in a cavity above the gill chamber. This contains a labyrinth of bony plates covered with a membrane rich in blood-vessels, which absorb oxygen direct from air

(top left)
Its flattened body and its method of swimming may make the **common discus,** or pompadour, look like a leaf floating in the water. An unwary smaller fish that passes by, however, may discover its real identity too late, when the large jaws suddenly open and seize it.

(top center)
Among the six hundred or so species of cichlids are many that are known for their brightness and coloring. One of the most striking is the **angelfish** of South America, a favorite of collectors. Although the young angelfish is a typical cichlid, the adult is unlike the other members of this family in form and habits. Note the tapering fins.

(top right)
One of the pompadour fishes from the Amazon basin, the brilliantly colored and barred **green discus** has peculiar breeding habits. The female lays her eggs on stones. When the young hatch, she transfers them to the leaves of water plants, where they hang by threads. Three days later, when they can swim freely, the young move to the parents' bodies, where they feed on a secretion from the skin.

(right)
Its outstanding feature, that of meeting mouth-to-mouth with extended lips, was sufficient reason for naming this fish the **kissing gourami.** One of the labyrinth fishes, it is native of Southeast Asia and some of the adjacent islands.

(below)
By a complicated dance the male **three-spined stickleback** leads the female to the nest he has constructed. Arriving at the nest he induces the female, by nodding movements of his head, to enter and lay her eggs.

gulped when at the surface of the water. These special organs enable the fishes to live in water so low in oxygen that it would otherwise be lethal.

The walking fish, formerly called the climbing perch, of India and South-east Asia, will travel from one pool to another, using its spiny-edged gillplates as "feet", progressing with a rocking motion at speeds of up to ten feet a minute. Related African species have a similar ability. These fishes are often found in forks of trees and bushes, and it used to be thought they had climbed there. We now know that such fishes have been cached there by birds, such as crows.

The spectacular Siamese fighting fish are labyrinth fishes, as are the "kissing" gourami of South-east Asia.

Most labyrinth fishes build nests of bubbles. The male takes air into his mouth, and blows a bubble of a sticky secretion to the surface. This is repeated, again and again, until a nest several inches in diameter is formed. The male and female embrace, the male fertilizing the eggs as they are laid, and subsequently he gathers them in his mouth from the bottom, and blows them into the nest. The nest is guarded by the male, as are the young until able to swim freely.

Snakeheads and Sticklebacks

SNAKEHEADS (FAMILY CHANNIDAE) OF AFRICA and South-east Asia, are so named for their snakelike appearance, enhanced by a protruding lower jaw and a tubular nostril. Ranging from six inches to three feet long, they are air-breathers like the labyrinth fishes; but the accessory breathing chamber is a simple cavity lined with a membrane equipped with a mass of fine veins. The eggs, when laid, float at the surface, and they and the young are guarded by the males. In some areas snakeheads are caught for market.

Several species of sticklebacks (family Gasterosteidae) are entirely confined to the Northern Hemisphere. The three-spined stickleback is found throughout this hemisphere in both salt and fresh water. Most sticklebacks have a series of bony plates along the sides of the body; they are armed with a varying number of spines and the rear part of the body is slender. The three-spined stickleback is famous for its breeding habits: the male builds a nest of aquatic plants glued together by threads of sticky material secreted by the kidneys. At the same time his hue grows brighter and a red patch appears on his throat. In the course of a complicated courtship he leads the female to the nest, which she enters to lay her eggs. Several females may contribute their eggs to

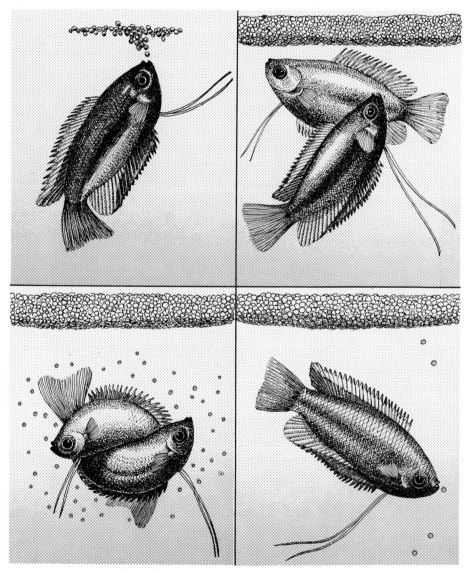

Some fresh-water fishes build **nests of bubbles.** They take air into the mouth at the surface, and the air bubbles become surrounded by fluids from the mouth. These bubbles harden on contact with the water, so that, when released, they float to the surface and stick together. The eggs are then placed on the lower surface of the bubble raft.

When the swamps and small streams dry up during periods of drought, the **African lungfish** (above and upper right) retires into the mud and fashions a cocoon around itself. Since it is an air-breather, it leaves a breathing hole in the cocoon. There it remains until the rains come to replenish the water in its habitat. Of the six species of lungfish, the most primitive is the Australian lungfish (bottom right).

this nest—which the male then guards. He keeps them aerated by fanning water over them with his fins. He cleans them from time to time, and when the young are hatched he guards them also until they are able to swim away on their own.

Spiny Eels, Swamp Eels and Lungfish

SPINY EELS (FAMILY MASTACEMBELIDAE) range throughout Africa and tropical Asia. They have elongated bodies, fifteen inches to three feet long, with a number of spines in front of the dorsal fin. The front of the head appears to consist of three lobes because of two tubular nostrils on the snout. One species is known as the elephant trunk fish because of its extremely long prehensile snout. Many spiny eels are air-breathers and can survive in mud or stagnant water indefinitely.

Swamp eels (family Symbranchidae) are smaller but lack the spines and they also lack paired fins. Their distribution is much the same as that of spiny eels but they are also found in tropical America. The best-known is the rice eel, two and one-half feet long, of South-east Asia, where it is sometimes used for food. It has also been introduced into Hawaii. Swamp eels pass the dry season in deep cavities in the mud very much in the way that lungfishes survive.

Lungfish (order Dipneusti) are found in limited areas in Australia, Africa and South America. They are remarkable for their ability to live in stagnant water, using lungs as well as gills for breathing. When the rivers and swamps dry up the lungfishes burrow into the mud where they form a kind of cocoon and go into a state of suspended animation until the rains come again. Their ability to survive without water is exemplified by the African lungfish, which has been known to survive for as long as four years out of water. While within the mud-cocoon the lungfish loses weight and also decreases in length but quickly makes up for this once it becomes active again.

► *The fascinating community of small animals and plants found in still pond waters.*

Pond Life

Picture to yourself a small woodland valley with, running through it, a slow-moving brook that periodically floods over its banks and which has created marshy areas here and there along its course. It may continue to flow in this fashion for a very long time, until suddenly, perhaps within days or even hours, something obstructs its passage. It could have been an earthslide or a diversion of the stream bed; it might have been the work of beavers or a structure from the hand of man. No matter what its cause, once the brook is checked the small valley will begin to fill. If the obstruction is not a large one, however, the accumulated water may cover no more than a few acres to a depth of six or seven feet before excess water is released as an overflow. This is how a pond can be born.

Although a pond may achieve its maximum size rapidly, it will take many years for it to assume a settled maturity, in which state it can remain for a long time. Eventually, however, the pond's size and productivity will diminish. Its banks will fill in and vegetation creep out from the shores; the silty bottom will gradually build toward the surface, and some day it will be no more. The region may come to resemble very closely what it had been hundreds of years before the marshy stream was changed into a pond. Such is the life of a pond; by its very nature it cannot be permanent.

Since ponds can be found almost everywhere, they provide most people with an excellent place to observe and enjoy natural life. In the winter many forms of life continue, although at a slower rate, beneath the icy surface; but by summer the pond is a hub of activity, with frogs leaping, turtles sunning and muskrats busily building a home for the season. The lightning-fast **dragonflies** pictured above (top right) look just about the same as their ancestors did millions of years ago, according to the fossil record. Immature dragonflies, or nymphs, that live in the pond leave it when they are grown, but the adults lay their eggs in the water and may stay nearby to feed on the abundant supply of flying insects.

Characteristics of a Pond

Is THERE A DIFFERENCE between a pond and a lake? Any difference is difficult to define. In fact, so far no scientific definition has been provided. One could say that a lake is a large expanse of water while a pond is a small piece of water. But what is meant by large or small—how do you measure it? The best definition appears to be that a pond is so small that its edges are not appreciably eroded by wave action. But I think we must accept the fact that so far on the basis of available information it is not really possible to distinguish between the two.

There is no such thing as a "typical" pond. Ponds are not only of many different sizes; they vary enormously in almost every way possible, and their character depends a great deal on their location and the nature of their surroundings. Geographical location, altitude and the type of soil are all important factors. A pond surrounded by open meadow can be expected to be very different from one lying within a dense forest. And a stagnant pond, or a polluted one, will be quite unlike a pond whose water is clean, well oxygenated and being continually changed through inflows and outflows.

Is the Water Acid or Alkaline?

Although the plants and animals pictured in this chapter come from many different ponds, we are going to assume that they come from one healthy woodland pond. Even if examples of the living things dealt with here cannot be found in your local pond it is certain that related forms will be; for the forms of life chosen for this chapter are from clean, mature ponds within the reach of an inquisitive naturalist. The creatures and plants described here are only a few of the enormous variety of anchored, drifting, gliding, crawling and flying life that is associated with any pond.

The gentle sloping hills that surround our pond contribute to its welfare and productivity. Aquatic plants get their nourishment from the mineral compounds which are brought to the pond by the runoff after every rainfall and, eventually, settle on the bottom. After a rain the water will be opaque as a result of the disturbance of the bottom by inflowing currents of rainwater, and because of new material just added to it. The muddy bottom from which plants grow usually is well cultivated by natural forces—nutrients are overturned constantly and mixed until they can be used.

Here and there springs feed the pond; but its level will remain fairly constant. The water level probably rises in spring with melting snows and rains, and undoubtedly lowers during late summer when evaporation removes quantities of water in the form of vapor.

The most variable characteristic of the pond is its temperature. Dur-

The **caddis fly larva** creeps about on the bottom of the pond. By secreting a sticky substance from its body, it can glue sand and small sticks together, making a tube home for itself.

(right)
Herons patrol the shallows, wading silently along and capturing small fish.

ing winter, thick ice usually forms over its still surface, killing many of the less hardy forms of life. However, unless the water is so shallow or the winter extremely bitter, a pond will not freeze solid. Water is unique among liquids in that when it cools to 4° Centigrade it begins to expand again and therefore becomes less dense. As the surface water cools, therefore, it floats on the warmer water below and insulates it from the cold air. The temperature of the water at the bottom of the pond thus only rarely falls to the freezing point. All other liquids continue to contract and get denser as they fall below 4° C., and so the coldest liquid sinks and it freezes from the bottom upwards. If water acted in this way, ponds would soon freeze solid in the winter.

The Pond Population

WHILE THE POND IN WINTER may seem deceptively still, life goes on, albeit slowly, in the mud on the floor of the pond. Because the temperature is low, the activities of the animals are considerably lessened and many creatures hide themselves away in the mud at the bottom in a state of suspended animation. Frogs and some of the larger water beetles act in this way and require so little oxygen in this state that their hold on life can be maintained by the small amounts that diffuse in their bodies. Fishes live quite happily under the ice but tend to float lazily among the vegetation. Such food as they need is supplied by plants, and by those small animals that remain active under the ice.

Such creatures as water fleas, cyclops, water mites and other small arthropods can always be found moving about in the water, although most of them spend the winter as eggs or encysted adults in the mud at the bottom.

Pond populations often change suddenly as a result of seasonal extremes, and some people are puzzled by this fact which contrasts sharply with the greater constancy of the populations that inhabit very large, deep lakes where conditions do not change readily. The lack of currents other than those caused by wind results in a gradual heating of the water that can lead to widespread lethal conditions. For instance, after a stretch of sunny weather the surface of a pond may feel hot to the touch, a condition that will force fishes and other water dwellers to seek the deepest and most shaded parts.

The variety of life that a pond will support can change a great deal from year to year because it is affected by changes in the supply of nutrients, and also by extremes of temperature. Some years will be "good" and others "bad" for certain plants and animals. All this means that under certain conditions populations of specific living things increase prolifically or decrease until they are scarcely in evidence. Sometimes a pond becomes bright green, brown or even reddish with the "bloom" of minute organisms. As with any population increase, the

(below left)
Alders fare best in moist soil, and so a pond's edge is an ideal growing place. They help to resist erosion and add fertilizing nitrates to the soil.

(below right)
Muskrats use the cattails that grow along the pond for construction purposes. In this photograph, taken on Long Island, New York, a **muskrat house** is built in castle fashion, with a pond for a moat.
Courtesy of the American Museum of Natural History

plants or animals that are so numerous will suddenly find themselves without adequate supplies of food and oxygen, and wholesale deaths occur. At times, when small forms of life die in untold numbers, their decaying bodies, microscopic though they may be, set free poisons that have a disastrous effect on the fishes, shrimps and other inhabitants of the pond. Then, quite as quickly, the situation returns to normal, and the pond will be found to be supporting its usual populations once again.

Only rarely do these population "explosions" affect the water for any length of time. On the other hand, a pond that becomes seriously polluted with industrial wastes will not support life for long, and such a small body of water cannot recover easily from even minor pollution. Find a pond beside a pulp mill into which wood wastes are poured, and you will find water that is almost void of life. Ponds from which cattle drink often are severely polluted from the animals' waste products.

Plant Life

B UT OUR POND is a healthy one, with a great variety of plants and animals forming a complex and interrelated community. Pond water is enriched by mineral salts and nitrates drawn from decayed leaves and animal remains, as the surrounding soil is washed down by the stream. Water plants derive nourishment in liquid form from these substances, not only through the surface of their stems and leaves, but also through their roots; and it is converted into vegetable tissue by the plant's natural chemical processes in which chlorophyll plays an important part. Starch is also produced, and stored in the plant itself to provide a kind of long-term food reserve for the plant. The numerous water fauna breathe the released oxygen. Where weeds are, animal life will be found. The vegetation on the slopes above the pond is little influenced by the water below, but closer to the pond's edge trees and shrubs such as willows and alders grow well in the moist soil; right at the water's edge these give way to semi-aquatic plants—smaller vegetation that grows in very wet earth. Here are the bulrushes, pickerel weeds and horsetails, some of them growing up from the muddy bottom through a few inches of water to emerge into air. Although these plants have rather pulpy, non-woody stems, they stand erect and often form dense masses of vegetation around the shoreline. Here frogs, newts, snakes and small birds find refuge from larger predators.

Where the water is deeper, fewer plants rise above the surface; but many climb just high enough to allow their leaves to reach the water film where they float on the surface, exposed to the air and sunshine. The water lilies are best known among these, but others such as water hyacinth may also be present. Some of the smallest of seed plants, too, the duckweeds, can be expected. Greater duckweed possesses

A pond contains many plant and animal communities, not only in the water but also on the surface and around the edge. This bright green **algae,** for example, growing on the surface with the other water plants will supply both food and oxygen for many animal inhabitants.

several small, waxy leaves that look almost like a miniature clover. Beneath each is a cluster of roots, but these roots never touch the bottom of the pond. Instead, they are suspended in the water from which they extract not only moisture but dissolved nitrates, an essential plant food. Another example of this is frog-bit, a plant having flat, rounded leaves that float on the top of the pond, roots hanging down or submerged, never taking root on the bottom. In the autumn this interesting weed develops thick, pointed shoots, which break off and settle in the mud without taking root. They lie dormant until springtime, when they rise to the surface and become new plants. The surface film supports flat, floating leaves such as those of the frog-bit, while the water below supports the spreading branches of the feathery or trailing types of plants. The stiff woody stems are unnecessary to buoyant water weeds that spread their pliant branches, their watery element giving continuous shelter and support. Submerged weeds always display small, finely cut, or grasslike leaves that yield to the movement of the water.

Long ago one of the first microscopists, Anton van Leeuwenhoek, looked at these roots out of curiosity and discovered them to be covered with small creatures that had found there a good lodging and feeding place. A related plant, Wolffia, has the distinction of being the smallest flowering plant on the face of the earth but it would never be recognized as a relative of a great tree. This plant, sometimes called water-meal, has no roots or stem, and its flowers are only minute ruptures of the upper surface of its tiny floating leaves. Duckweeds and water-meal reproduce most commonly by budding; that is, the plant bodies divide in two. When conditions are right, whole shores can sometimes appear to be dressed in a coat of green, as a result of millions upon millions of these little plants nestling against one another in the shallow water around the pond's edge.

In the deeper water, pondweeds break the water film only to flower; all their other activities are carried on beneath the surface. Pondweeds grow rapidly in the spring and early summer, and after flowering, their delicate stems become reduced and they then produce fewer leaves. In the early warm months, however, ponds may become so choked with pondweeds as to make the passage of small boats almost impossible. When they die and disintegrate later on, the water grows murky with masses of particles of decayed organic material.

A whole company of submerged aquatic plants covers the pond bottom; some of them are long lasting, but others grow rapidly and soon disappear. Tape grass, water-crowfoot, arrowheads, hornwort and the carnivorous bladderwort with its many traps for small swimming creatures are only a few of the aquatic plants that grow in most ponds.

Smaller than these are the algae and their relatives, all very simple plants composed either of single cells or colonies of loosely organized

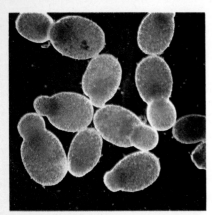

The smallest of the duckweeds, **water-meal** consists only of tiny leaves that bud continually to produce more of their own kind. Notice the different stages of development in the picture.

Water lilies are by far the most popular water plants in the garden pool or ornamental pond. The large leaves, like platters resting on the surface, offer shady places for fish, frogs and newts.

cells. Despite their simplicity, they, too, assist in providing substances that are essential to a well-balanced community. By means of a green pigment, chlorophyll, plants create sugar from water and carbon dioxide using sunlight as their energy. Small grazing animals in the pond, and larger ones, too, devour the plants and in their bodies "burn" the food by means of the oxygen they breathe in through gills or lungs. Since animals give off carbon dioxide as waste, it can readily be seen that a complete cycle has been affected; namely, an oxygen-carbon dioxide cycle involving both plants and animals. A pond is an entire community, with its inhabitants enjoying a mutual exchange of materials. Naturally, the surface of the pond is not an impenetrable boundary, at least to the gases dissolved in water, for oxygen can enter from the atmosphere, and carbon dioxide is capable of diffusion outward into the air. Nevertheless, it is probable that animal life in the pond might suffer if plants did not contribute their gift of oxygen, and many aquatic animals certainly would starve if they could not find plant material to eat.

Not all animals graze upon plants, of course, but some do, and they in turn are fed upon by predators that later may be eaten by other predators, and so on until a large carnivorous animal is reached. In every case, there has been a transfer not only of materials, but also of energy. This energy originates in the sun, but becomes locked in a sugar molecule by a green plant through the process already described. A food chain is complex, and can relate almost every form of life within a pond to every other, for life here consists mainly of plants, vegetarians and predators. The pond, then, with its confining boundaries of shore, bottom and surface film represents a world in miniature and is worthy of concentrated study by anyone with a bit of curiosity about the natural world in which he lives.

Duckweed is a truly aquatic plant. It drifts on the surface and sends down clusters of short roots that hang free in the water from an exceedingly short stem. At times, one or two minute flowers are borne at the edges of the leaves.

The Bottom Dwellers

A POND IS PRACTICALLY DEVOID of currents as a rule and most of its animal life is well adapted to a mode of life that calls for swimming or drifting along in quiet water. The "streamlining" so valuable to creatures that live in fast-flowing brooks and rivers is not necessary to the pond's inhabitants, many of which progress by crawling over its bottom. Many bottom dwellers in ponds are bulky and lack the ability to move rapidly, although they may be highly successful in the capture of prey. On the bottom of the pond or on the stems of water plants one can often see what looks like a small bundle of sticks moving awkwardly. If you look more closely, at one end you may see a small head and the forelegs of the larva of the caddis fly. If you were to break open the sticks you would find a hollow chamber in which the larva lives. Without the home of sticks, which it glues together with a secretion from its own body, the wormlike larva would soon fall prey to fishes, newts and other predators. The caddis fly larva will also use small stones or snail shells to construct its home. Later, the larva will swim to the surface and use its jaws to cut its way out to emerge as a mothlike fly.

Some of the dragonfly nymphs are lumpy creatures and not at all as streamlined as those nymphs which hug the stream bed of a swift brook; but they are equally successful in the capture of food. The nymph wanders at random over the aquatic vegetation until it comes upon its unwary prey. Then, when it is close enough it shoots out its extensible, powerfully hinged jaws. In this way it can capture not only other insects but even small fishes and tadpoles. These nymphs are well adapted to an aquatic life, and the leaflike appendage that many of them have is their breathing apparatus. They use it to take in water which, after its oxygen has been extracted, is expelled. The process provides the nymph with a system of pulse-jet propulsion which sends it forward with a jerking motion.

The nymph eventually reaches a stage of development that causes it to climb up the stem of a water plant to await transformation. At this stage the nymph will have developed the series of spiracles on each side of its body by which it is enabled to breathe air, and so get sufficient oxygen from the atmosphere. It is then soon to become an adult.

An adult dragonfly, once emerged from its aquatic immaturity, remains associated with the pond because it must lay its eggs in water. Furthermore, as an active predator, it finds an ample supply of winged victims flying over the water; it can be seen throughout summer pursuing with erratic flight midges and flies too small to be easily seen by human eyes.

Possibly the most common insect larvae found in ponds are those of midges. These small wormlike creatures usually inhabit bottom mud or construct tubular dwellings from bits of debris on submerged surfaces. Often a sunken log or rock will be covered with thousands of brown lines about a quarter of an inch long. Upon close examination

(bottom left)
Damselflies are related to the dragonflies and, like their larger cousins, they remain motionless until they dart over the water to catch a small fly. They can also fly backwards and may be seen dancing over the water when they are in a courting mood.

(bottom center)
Without its house of sticks the **caddis fly larva** probably would not escape its predators. Small stones and shells are sometimes used in the construction.

(bottom right)
The **water moccasin** is sometimes called the cottonmouth because of the whiteness of its mouth when open and about to strike. Moccasins feed mainly on fish and other animals found in or around lakes and ponds. When grown they reach a length of about five feet.

Dragonflies catch their prey on the wing. They have the speed and the aerobatic efficiency needed to outfly many insects. One species of Australian dragonfly has been recorded flying over a measured distance at 60 m.p.h.

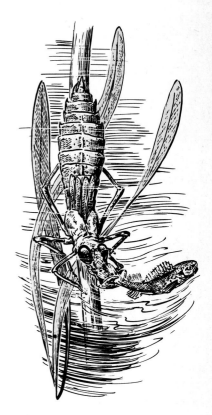

Underwater conflict results when a **dragonfly larva** feeds on a passing minnow.

these can be seen to be tiny tubes. If a tube is opened carefully, a larva will wriggle free. Some of these midge larvae are a brilliant red; many others are green or a duller yellow or brown. They feed upon organic matter that they extract from the mud by means of their clawed front legs. They breathe by extending posterior gill filaments into the water to allow an exchange of oxygen and waste gases. Midge larvae are enormously important in food chains; when the stomachs of some fishes are examined they are found to contain hundreds or even thousands of these larval insects packed in large masses. Despite the activities of predators, midges survive in fantastic numbers and at times emerge into the air as grey, swaying clouds of winged adults.

There is one pond dweller that never leaves the bottom and is quite unable to protect itself, yet it is seldom eaten. This is a small flattened worm, Planaria, so dark in hue that it perfectly matches the background of sticks and stones upon which it crawls, making it almost invisible even when one is searching for it. It seems to prefer the undersurfaces of pebbles near the shore, and positively shuns the light. It moves slowly, flowing over surfaces with a gliding motion produced by the beating of thousands of tiny hairs on its undersurface. Planaria generally feeds upon dead matter, but seems to prefer fairly fresh animal substances. This worm can be kept in a dark container and fed on bits of fresh liver more or less indefinitely; but since it will not tolerate polluted water, any uneaten meat must be removed before it can decay. Planaria has many curious characteristics, and any good textbook on zoology will suggest a number of highly interesting observations and experiments that may be performed with these simple creatures. For instance, bits of them can be grafted together; their mouths are like vacuum cleaner hoses; they have "crossed eyes"; and their eggs, deposited in cocoons on stalks, resemble balloons on strings. These creatures are free-living relatives of parasitic worms which live in the digestive tract of sheep and many other animals.

Some **sundews** attract large insects to pollinate their flowers while capturing smaller ones with the hairs on their leaves. Adhesive secretions from the hairs hold the insect until it is digested.

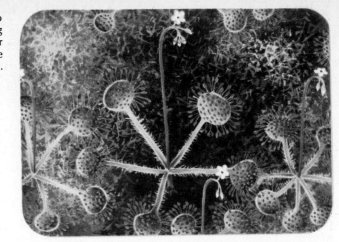

Colonies of hydra contain several generations at once. Besides the adult hydra, with its tentacles that emerge to paralyze and hold the prey (2-3), the buds (1) of the new generation are also present. In some species the buds, or medusae, drop off and swim away.

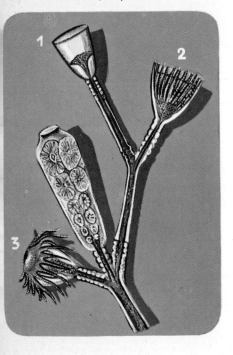

(opposite page)
The short-tailed weasel, better known as an **ermine** (lower left), stalking the **red-backed vole** (extreme right) is a hunter always on the prowl. Because of its relatively high metabolism, it must feed frequently in winter as well as summer; and so, to be more effective when stalking prey during the snowy season, when cover is lacking, its pelt turns white. Unfortunately, this also means that it often winds up as someone's wrap or fur coat. The vole shares much of its range with the weasel and consequently is a common prey for it. Majestic Mount Katahdin looms in the background.

The Tiny Hydra

ANOTHER VERY SIMPLE CREATURE is the hydra, which is related to marine animals such as the jellyfishes and sea anemones. Although hydras can be very plentiful in many ponds, they are too small to be found by searching among the underwater plants to which they attach themselves. When fully extended they are readily visible, measuring up to one and a half inches in length; but when disturbed their method of self-protection is to contract in size until they are tiny, transparent globules of jelly. If, however, a portion of duckweed is removed from the pond and placed in a glass container full of water, any hydras which are present will soon stretch out their tentacles and become visible and available for study. Their structure comprises a cylindrical body which terminates at one end in a bunch of tentacles, whose number may be as few as seven, or as many as a dozen. Situated at the point from which the tentacles radiate is the only body opening which accepts food and expels all waste. At the extremity of each tentacle there is a retractile thread containing a paralyzing fluid which is used to inject the animal's prey; this stuns it sufficiently to allow the hydra's remaining tentacles to be brought into action to complete the immobilization; thus the disabled prey can be conveyed to the hydra's "mouth" and then to the simple digestive chamber. Small creatures such as daphnia, the so-called water fleas, are the principal items in the hydra's diet; but newly-hatched fish are also taken when they come within range of the encircling tentacles. When an abundance of food is available, hydras reproduce prolifically by budding. Tiny buds appear on the body and soon develop tentacles enabling the young hydra to feed independently of the parent, although it is not uncommon for parent and offspring to compete for the same victim. The young hydra soon reaches a size approaching that of the parent, whereupon it separates and floats away as a

completely independent creature. Sexual reproduction occurs but this does not necessarily mean that two separate hydras have to be involved. An individual hydra may play a bisexual role, in which case sperms are released from sacs at the mouth end of the body and these swim to the base of the body where the egg cells are located when fertilization takes place.

Carrying Air Underwater

SOME OF THE MOST UNLIKELY creatures can be found in ponds—life forms more usually associated with terrestrial environments. The water spider is such an example and quite remarkable in the manner in which it has adapted itself to living underwater. A lung-breather like its landlocked relatives, this small spider has a body and legs thickly clothed in fine hairs. When the creature descends into the water, the air trapped among these hairs forms a reserve which the spider is able to draw upon while swimming about its business.

In order to remain submerged for long periods of time the spider constructs an air reservoir in the following manner: selecting a couple of underwater plant stems growing close together, the spider spins a silken platform between them. This done it rises and, raising its abdomen above the water surface, traps a bubble of air between its hind legs. This is conveyed to the web platform and released on the underside where it becomes trapped. Successive visits to the surface followed by the release of fresh bubbles of air under the platform result in an upward pressure of air, which at length forms a little diving bell. In this the spider lurks, occasionally making a sortie to capture prey in the shape of daphnia or other small creatures which are taken back to the diving bell to be consumed. The two sexes each build their own air chamber, and the female converts the top of hers into a separate compartment in which her eggs are laid.

Water spiders are not unique in carrying air underwater; many insects, too, have perfected this technique in a variety of ways. Creep-

(bottom left)
Mosquito larvae hang from the surface film in a pond, breathing through their tails.

(bottom center)
With its paddlelike hind legs, the **whirligig beetle** is able to dive as well as swim at the surface. Because the air it carries down gives it buoyancy, the beetle must grasp a bit of vegetation to keep from rising with the air bubble.

(bottom right)
Water boatmen lay their eggs on the surface of a solid object, such as a log, a stone or a concrete wall. They are hunters of other water insects and, being active and powerful swimmers, can often overtake their prey.

(left)
Inside the **fresh-water mussel** shell millions of tiny hairs beat steadily, creating a current that sweeps water and the plants and creatures it carries into the shell. When this food is captured, it is transported by sheets of mucus to the hidden mouth, where it is swallowed.

(below)
Compared to the swift aquatic insects, the creeping **water bug** is a veritable laggard. Much of its time is spent crawling over submerged vegetation, where it finds small victims that can easily be caught. An air breather, it carries a supply of air underwater, which gives its body a silvery coating.

ing water bugs come to the surface from time to time to take fresh air which they store in the space between the body and wing-covers, and among hairs to which bubbles adhere. The whirligig beetle, normally a surface dweller, carries an extra supply about its head and a very large bubble trapped in hairs on its rear end. This makes it so buoyant that it has to cling to underwater vegetation in order to remain submerged. A large predatory diving beetle is completely at home below the surface and rises only occasionally to take in air. Its big eyes easily detect movement of its many possible prey, which include other insects, tadpoles, small eels and fishes.

Other aquatic insects, tied to the outer world through their need for air, are the water bugs, back-swimmers, water striders, water scorpions and water boatmen. The larvae of many kinds of mosquitoes and gnats need to rise to the surface for their air supplies. But one species has developed an extraordinary method of obtaining its air without having to undertake these often dangerous excursions. It has a breathing tube which it inserts into the stems of water plants to take the oxygen it needs. Both the slender and the flattened water scorpions receive their air periodically through "snorkels" formed by a cluster of long hairs and filaments. Apart from their grasping front legs, these insects bear no resemblance to their poisonous namesakes. Water boatmen carry their air under translucent wing-covers. These brightly-hued little animals scull themselves along underwater with rapid movements of a pair of oarlike legs. Their large eyes are well constructed to catch even the slightest movements of would-be pursuers. Water boatmen use two front pairs of legs to sweep bottom sediment into their mouths where they sift out small plants and worms. There is another aquatic bug, the water measurer, which is so slender that it seems to be just a knotted bit of thread. The measurer frequents open sunny ponds where it darts about the surface as if it were measuring the area. Pond skaters and measurers can walk on the water because the surface film is elastic.

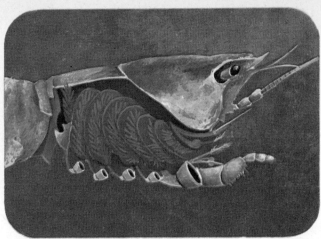

(top left)
Prey for some of the larger fish, **crayfish** are themselves useful scavengers and predators, seizing food in their claws. They frequently crawl, but a few violent thrusts of their tails can send them backwards through the water at great speed.

(top right)
Large crustaceans, **crayfish** inhabit many ponds, living in the muddy banks or scavenging at the bottom. They breathe by means of gills that are attached to the legs.

This is made very noticeable by the way in which the surface film is forced upwards by many insects which stretch it tent-wise as they rise to take in air at the surface.

Compared with water boatmen, which are among the most active of pond dwellers, there are other creatures that hardly move at all. Half-buried in the soft bottom the hard bulk of a freshwater mussel, its shell slightly agape, might be seen. Inactive though it may seem to be on the outside, a great deal is going on within. Millions of tiny hairs arranged across the several layers of gills beat steadily, causing a continuous current of water to flow in, bringing with it numerous small items of floating food. The tiny plants and animals thus introduced are captured on sheets of mucus that flow towards the hidden mouth, and swallowed without cessation. Up under the hinge of the animal, a simple heart beats sluggishly, and it is interesting to know that the mussel's intestine passes directly through it. The entire animal does move at times, pushing out a ponderous, muscular foot into the bottom. By retracting this foot suddenly, the mussel is able to progress slowly across the floor of the pond from one feeding ground to another.

Snails, Shrimps and Crayfishes

ANOTHER MOLLUSK, a relative of the mussel, is the snail. On the front part of the body of this curious creature there are two sensory tentacles. In the great pond snail they are flat and triangular; in the freshwater winkle, threadlike. An eye is located at the base of each tentacle and underneath a mouth. The lower part of the body is called the foot. The internal organs, attached to the shell by muscles, lie in the part of the body hidden by the shell. There are two groups of freshwater snails, the operculates and the pulmonates. Operculates breathe air filtered from the water by means of gills. There is a flat horny plate at the end of the body with which they seal the shell's

entrance. Pulmonate snails breathe air into their lungs, rising to the water's surface to do so.

As anyone who has kept snails in an aquarium will testify, they have no difficulty in reproducing, for each individual has both male and female systems in its body. As a result, eggs can be fertilized even when only one snail is present, and transparent egg masses will soon be seen attached to the stems of aquatic plants and to stones. A microscopic view of these eggs will show many snails developing; at first they appear to be not at all snail-like, but after a short time their tiny, delicate shells become recognizable. Eventually they break from their gelatinous capsules, and take up a free life in the pond, scraping off and eating the minute algae that coat almost every submerged surface.

Close to the bottom where snails feed, other small but complex creatures can be seen kicking about among decaying vegetable matter. Under magnification these little animals show a surprisingly high state of structural development; they are freshwater shrimps called Gammarus. While they are much smaller than salt water shrimps they have nearly all the same basic features and can provide hours of fascination to the lucky person able to study them under a low power microscope. They will thrive in a small aquarium so long as plenty of food in the form of decaying plant and animal matter is made available. Gammarus are hungry scavengers that will eat almost any form of organic debris, although they browse about in what appears to be an exasperated fashion that suggests they are never really satisfied.

Large crustaceans also inhabit most ponds, living either in the muddy banks, or as wandering scavengers crawling about the bottom. These are the crayfishes, always on the alert and ready to investigate any possible source of food, and yet constantly on the defensive against larger animals that might, in their turn, regard the crayfish as fair game. A crayfish is largely bluff, and although it can produce a hard nip with its claws, it is far more likely to escape with a violent thrust of its tail

(top left)
The **roach** feeds on small aquatic insects and small crustaceans. In its pursuit of food it avoids contact with the pike, for which the roach is a likely meal.

(top right)
Like the predatory pike, the **bream** swims in shoals. In the United States the name "bream" is often given to several kinds of minnows and sunfish.

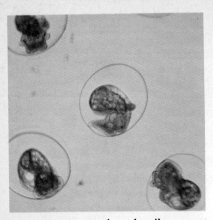

Egg masses of pond snails are most abundant in the spring, although they can be found until early autumn. Young snails do not leave the gelatinous egg mass until their shells have one or two whorls.

Fresh-water shrimp can be found in the bottom debris of any pond. In an area of approximately ten square feet there may be thousands of these small animals. They are common items of food for other pond dwellers.

than it is to fight. When a crayfish walks over the bottom, it rests on eight pairs of tiptoes, holding its large claws out in front to pick up pieces of food. Smaller claws and several pairs of mouth-parts are constantly working, sampling and rejecting bits and pieces of matter that cannot readily be consumed. If a crayfish is seized by one of its appendages, particularly a walking leg, an immediate reflex action causes muscles to contract and sever the leg at a specific breaking point, leaving it in the grasp of a predator while the crayfish dashes off to live and fight and prey another day.

The largemouth black bass of American waters, which has been introduced with some success to British ponds and lakes, is an animal that, like the European pike, would attack a crayfish with gusto. This popular game fish is one of the most active and voracious of predatory fishes. Rudd, roach and bream, which usually swim in shoals, inhabit the same waters as the pike; the food of the former fishes which are all members of a very widespread group, the Cyprinids, consists of small creatures, mostly aquatic insects and various small crustaceans. In searching it out, however, they need to give the pike a wide berth, because this large predator is likely to make a meal of any other living creature in its vicinity.

Fishes of the Pond

ONE FISH WHICH LIVES in the muddiest pond water is the tench. It feeds on worms and mollusks grubbed from the mud and clears up dead and decaying material which would otherwise foul the pond. In this respect it resembles the American "bullhead", a species of catfish. Waiting in woody patches where their subtly striped bodies go unnoticed are some of the swiftest and most ferocious fishes, the perch. Ponds make an excellent habitat for this fish. The perch, like its American counterparts, is an active and voracious fish often found swimming in shoals at the surface. When taken from its surroundings its markings appear very vivid with its green back, red fins and bold stripes; but this livery serves well as camouflage among the stems and foliage of underwater plants when the fish plays a waiting game for unsuspecting prey. Reaching a weight of from four to eight pounds it is a greedy feeder, being particularly fond of young fish and frogs.

Three-spined sticklebacks are also found in our pond lurking in tangles of water-weed. In shape these are elegantly distinctive, especially the male, whose iridescence is splashed with red. The stickleback is one of those unusual species whose males take on the task of parental care. He first of all digs a shallow pit as the chosen nest site. This he does by practically standing on his head, and sucking sand into his mouth. The stickleback swims away and deposits the sand elsewhere and returns for more until the pit is ready, and then builds a nest in it, using a green alga as building material. He defends his nest site and the territory nearby against all other male sticklebacks. A female entering the territory is recognized by her swollen body, swollen because of the ripe eggs she carries. If she is willing to be courted, she remains quite still with her body curved. The male then meets her with a zig-zag swim, indicating the nest by putting his mouth near the entrance. After entering the nest the female is stimulated to lay her eggs by the male nudging her at the base of the tail. Once the eggs are laid the female is driven away because otherwise she would eat them. The nest and eggs are protected from other wandering sticklebacks by the male.

Of course, other fishes are present and are often very numerous. Carp, chub, dace, roach and rudd abound in ponds while the ruffe, a relative of the perch, often swims in schools at the surface.

A convenient link between the fishes and our next life form, the amphibians, is supplied by the lung fish, the largest of which hails from Australia and reaches a length of six feet. The air or swim-bladder of this creature has become modified and operates as a lung. Living in the stagnant ponds formed along the course of the Mary River in Queensland, the lung fish has to withstand long periods during which the hot weather causes the water to become too foul for gill-breathing to oxygenate the system. With the aid of its lung it is able to obtain air supplies from the atmosphere by making periodic journeys to the surface, remaining submerged for up to half an hour between such replenishment trips.

Two other species of lung fish can be found in Africa and South America, each of them able to leave the water; without this ability they would be unable to endure the dry seasons that occur in the regions where they are to be found. During periods of sustained drought, perhaps several months, they remain coiled up in the mud within a chamber whose walls are formed from a secretion exuded for this purpose. Contact with the atmosphere for breathing purposes is made via a thin tube. The young are very like tadpoles for some weeks after hatching. The build and habits of the adult fish make them resemble giant salamanders.

(below left)
Broad-headed and equipped with strong jaws, **chubs** eat great numbers of small fish. During the spring many of them dig pits in stream bottoms and line them with stones and pebbles before laying their eggs.

(below right)
The **stickleback** goes through an elaborate routine in nest-building, courtship and mating, as well as in caring for the eggs and the young.

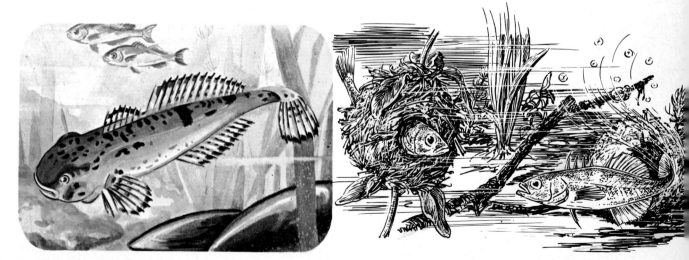

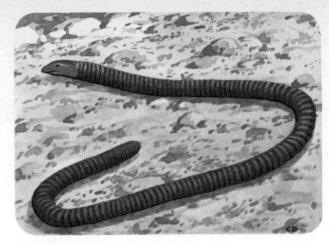

(top left)
Most of the 200 species of **salamanders** in the world are voiceless. Secretive creatures, they are often found hiding under stones and logs.

(top right)
Like frogs and toads, **caecilians** are amphibians. Legless, burrowing creatures, they look like large earthworms. Some lay eggs, while others give birth to living young.

Amphibian Inhabitants

ASCENDING THE SCALE OF LIFE from fishes to other, more highly developed, animals with backbones, the visitor to the pond will find it populated with amphibians or batrachians. These lie between the fishes and the reptiles on the scale of life and spend only a part of their lives as truly aquatic forms.

Amphibians were earlier inhabitants of our planet than reptiles, mammals and birds. They first appeared on the scene about 300 million years ago during the period in geological history known as the Devonian; there were fishes in seas, lakes, rivers and ponds; and there were insects crawling and flying. The earth itself was active, too; the howling winds were shaping the land, volcanic eruptions were creating mountains, islands, changing the courses of rivers and at the same time destroying much of what they had earlier created. Through this period the amphibians were formed, and from their stock other land vertebrates were created. When we examine the salamanders, newts, frogs and toads in the ponds it is worthwhile remembering their long history. They are creatures of ancient lineage whose ancestors were here before our own.

Amphibians are divided into three orders: the Anura or tailless batrachians (frogs and toads); the Urodela or Caudata (newts and salamanders); and the Apoda or limbless batrachians.

There are some 2,600 species of frogs and toads in the world and they are found in most temperate and tropical regions. They are absent only from snow-capped mountain tops, waterless deserts and some Pacific islands. In form, toads differ from frogs in having fat, squat bodies, short legs and a hopping walking gait. Frogs are more streamlined, faster moving creatures, with powerful hind legs that enable them to take long leaps; and far more aquatic.

Unlike frogs, toads do not rely on speed to escape their enemies;

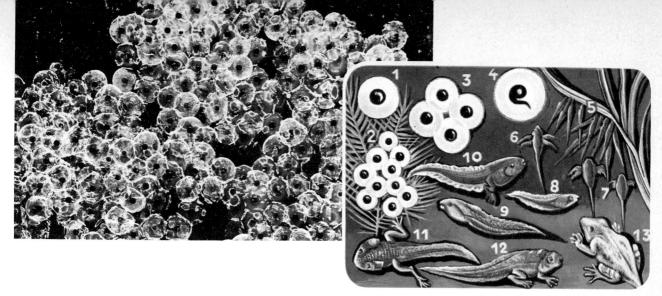

they make great use of camouflage by burying themselves, and also rely on a poison secreted by the parotoid gland situated behind the eyes, and smaller glands distributed over the body. A dog, cat or fox trying to swallow or eat a toad soon realizes its mistake, for the poison causes a burning sensation in the mouth that leaves the predator with no alternative but to drop the toad. The poison is hardly ever fatal to other animals—it is just rather unpleasant!

Every spring thousands of toads are killed on the roads and country lanes as they make their way toward the ponds where they spawn. The loss of such numbers makes no noticeable difference to the total number of toads because they are such prolific breeders; the marine toad, for example, produces about 35,000 eggs a year. In a few days a pond can become a mass of wriggling tadpoles, all of them feeding ravenously on algae and microscopic life. Within a month they look like miniature copies of their parents. With fully developed lungs able to breathe air, they leave the pond to find new pastures in dark ditches, or wet meadows or marshes. In these places they will live and grow until they are mature enough to migrate to the pond where they, in their turn, will lay their spawn.

True toads are found in all temperate and tropic regions with the exceptions of Australasia, Madagascar, and some of the Pacific islands. The green toad that is a native of Central Europe and Tibet has been found at an altitude of 15,000 feet in the Himalayas.

One of the smallest toads is Rose's toad; it grows to little more than an inch in length and is to be found in the mountainous districts near Capetown, South Africa. The oak toad, *Bufo quercicus,* of the south-eastern United States, may be even smaller—it is three-quarters of an inch to one and one-quarter inches long.

The tadpole is the best known of the immature amphibians, and the stages of its development from inactive egg to mature frog are known to many through home aquarium study. An adult frog will seldom stray very far from its "home pond". This is not only the place in which eggs must be laid; it is also a refuge from airborne predators or land predators, and it produces much of the food the frog must eat. On spring and summer nights the pond resounds with the calls of many frogs, one of the most vociferous of which in America is the bullfrog. It is of interest to note that in England there was no frog which could reasonably be called a bullfrog until 1936, when a few laughing frogs from the Balkans, introduced for study at the University of London, were liberated in Kent and subsequently spread with great rapidity over most of Romney Marsh.

Their presence in the area in such great numbers has resulted in an alarming reduction in the population of the native frog upon which they freely prey. A third species of frog, for long established in England, is the edible frog, whose original introduction has been believed to have occurred during the Roman occupation; this may indeed be true—but it is even more certain that other members of this species have been introduced from time to time during later periods of history.

The most striking of Australian frogs are the tree frogs, and some of the most bright-hued of all the world's tree frogs are those encountered in the Northern Territory of Australia. While these curious and interesting creatures spend their adult life among the foliage of shrubs and trees they are compelled, like most amphibians, to return annually to water in order to reproduce.

There are exceptions to every rule and the clawed frog, from South and tropical Africa, differs from the majority of amphibians in being entirely aquatic. Its eternal watery environment has resulted in the hind feet developing enormous webs between the sharply clawed toes, which give their owner the ability to propel through the water at a speed which astonishes those who are unfamiliar with the species.

Another exception to the general amphibian pattern is the Pipa or Surinam toad from northern South America and the West Indies. The adult female carries her eggs as a gelatinous mass on her back. Her back takes on a yielding consistency in the breeding season, and each egg fits down into its own little depression where it remains until metamorphosis is complete and a perfect toad emerges.

There are numerous different frogs, so numerous in fact that it would be impossible to describe them all adequately here. Appropriately, however, the true frogs of the genus *Rana* are very widely distributed inhabitants of ponds and lakes. Various member species are to be found in the ponds of North America, Central and South America, Eurasia, Africa and Northern Australia. They are also to be found in other water habitats, such as marshes, water meadows, streams and wet ditches.

Their basic diet usually consists of insects, slugs, earthworms and beetles; but some of the larger species have a more varied diet. The North American bullfrog is such a one; its diet is likely to include young water birds, ducklings, young turtles, besides such fishes as are

The **edible frog** is a European species that often lives where ponds are close together, enabling it to move from pond to pond and range over a fairly wide area. Apparently indifferent to the heat, it likes to bask in the rays of the sun.

too slow to escape its attacks—and it is not averse to making a meal of smaller and weaker members of its own species. But frogs, too, have their enemies; these include herons, egrets, snakes and otters, to mention just a few that hunt around ponds and lakes.

Breeding Patterns of Frogs

THE MATING HABITS of most true frogs are similar—at least to the extent that mating occurs in the water. The males will often produce a chorus of calls which seem to have three basic uses; there is a call used to attract and direct the females; a warning call used when one male accidentally seizes another male instead of a female; and, finally, there is the call a male makes when he intends to grip a female. Courtship starts when a female enters the water. The male swims around her making his "sexual call"; then grasping her he lies full length upon her back so that the female is compelled to carry him during the act of mating. The egg spawn is forced out, indeed, almost pumped out. As it is ejected, it is fertilized by sperm of the male. The spawn either floats freely in the water or becomes attached to water weeds. One frog, which is found in China, is a nest builder. The male of this species constructs a burrow in the bank of a pond with the aid of his nose. The female ejects her eggs in such a way that they enter the burrow, where they are left to hatch out of the way of predatory fishes and insects in the pond below.

The majority of frogs grow to sexual maturity within one year, and are known to live in a natural state for about five years. When brought up in captivity, with regular food—and safe from their natural enemies —they often live a good deal longer.

Those who wish to keep them in captivity will find them attractive pets which can be kept in good health if a few simple rules are followed.

For small specimens a glass aquarium of about eighteen inches square should be quite adequate. Cover the bottom with leaf mold and moss and provide a shallow vessel for water. Always provide pieces of tree bark, and stones from a pond, arranged to provide miniature caves where they can shelter. The top of the aquarium should have a tight-fitting lid to stop the inmates from escaping. It is a natural instinct of all animals to explore and frogs are no exception. If they escape into a room and cannot find water they will quickly die of dehydration. Their food is no problem; they relish earthworms, spiders, flies and other insects. Some species can be persuaded to eat pieces of raw meat as long as it is agitated in front of them. A warning here: the feeding drive of all frogs is directed by movement—if anything moves a frog will attack. It is advisable when keeping several frogs together to ensure that they are all of the same size, otherwise you will find very large frogs tend to overlook the distinction between their smaller brethren and insects—and your frog collection will diminish quickly. Keeping

Ponds and other bodies of water are **vital for frogs,** both for breeding and for protection from land predators and birds. In addition, frogs need water to keep their skin wet, for without moisture many would quickly die from dehydration.

frogs enables you to study at close quarters aspects of their behavior hidden from you in the open pond. Take advantage of this by keeping careful notes of what you observe.

Newts and Salamanders

PLENTY OF AMPHIBIANS besides frogs are associated with ponds, and in most European ponds you can easily see newts, which are a species allied to the Old World salamander. Like frogs and toads, most newts must pass part of their lives in a wet environment. Gilled newt larvae often abound in the quiet back reaches of swampy ponds. Here they can feed upon aquatic insects and other small animals until becoming sufficiently mature to emerge on land. During the time they are in the water, their feathery gills stand out conspicuously as the oxygen-bearing water blows through the fine filaments. At this stage there are other clear indications of the newts' descent from fishlike ancestors. Tiny pits can be seen about the head and sides; these are openings to a sensory organ—the lateral line—which is clearly seen in most fishes. After newts reach a certain stage of maturity, they lose their gills and crawl from the water to take up life in nearby banks, living under rocks and logs where sufficient moisture exists. Although the adults undergo a change of hue and lose their gills they closely resemble the young in general form.

The best time to observe newts is during the breeding season, because at other times they are terrestrial, hiding under leaves, stones and roots. If the pond is sufficiently clear one can easily watch the courtship display of the male, whose attractive and prominent crest along the back, and whose tail with its orange, red and black blotched underparts, make him immediately recognizable. To attract the female he nudges her with his head, blocks her path and vigorously vibrates his tail. By this method he is displaying himself fully to her. The purpose of this display is to put the female into the right mood for the mating, which will result in the eggs being fertilized within the female. The eggs are laid singly and are wrapped or enclosed in the leaves of such water plants as water speedwell, water ranunculus, or water startwort. The female is particular in her choice of leaves, feeling and smelling them before she deposits each egg. No doubt the leaves afford a certain amount of protection to the eggs from predators.

The development of all species of newts through the egg and tadpole stages is very similar. Temperature undoubtedly has an important effect on the rate of growth and development. Warmth speeds up the process. The tadpoles of the palmate newt in the high and cold altitudes of the Alps and Pyrenees take up to ten or twelve months to develop.

The oval-shaped egg consists of a clear jellylike envelope that surrounds and protects the embryo which is free to move about inside. In this jelly package the tadpole develops. The eyes appear first, then the

Feathery gills that absorb oxygen from the water are one connection between this **immature newt** and its fishlike ancestors. These gills eventually disappear as it approaches the adult stage. Both tadpole and adult newts live on a diet of small creatures.

mouth, followed by the feathery appendages which are the gills. Four weeks will pass before the tadpole frees itself by digesting the jelly. At first the tadpole is rather awkward in the water, since it takes several days for the limbs to become strong enough for efficient swimming. The tadpoles are carnivorous and feed on minute crustacea and the larvae of water insects. Adult newts, too, are carnivorous; insects of all kinds, earth worms, slugs and similar creatures provide a diet that is far from monotonous.

There is one notable non-conformist that must be mentioned here. The axolotl of Mexico is, to outward appearances, a large, gilled tadpole about seven inches long. But it differs from other tadpoles in being able to live and breed in this state through successive generations. In periods of drought, however, the gills and the dorsal and caudal fins disappear, and eyelids develop. The result is a terrestrial salamander which was known for many years in the United States without being suspected of any relationship to the axolotl of Mexico.

In America land turtles (more commonly referred to as terrapin in Europe) are sometimes so numerous and exist in such variety in some areas as to seem to be, locally, the dominant form of vertebrate life. A pond can support an astounding number of these animals—some of them of considerable size. Those turtles that are predominantly carnivorous are less numerous than those that are grazers or vegetarians, although even the latter will usually pick up such food as shrimps and worms when opportunity presents itself. Animals that eat both vegetation and meat are said to be omnivorous; this adjective certainly applies to painted turtles. These handsome reptiles are known to reach a size of over seven inches in length of shell. They are shy animals and seldom are seen closely. In some regions residents call them and their relatives, the red-bellied turtles, "sliders" because they slip into the water at the first sign of an approaching boat. Painted turtles spend most of their time in the water but can be seen sunning themselves on logs and

Leaving the water, the larva of the red spotted newt transforms into a **red eft,** the land form of this species. After remaining on land for one to three years, it returns to water and changes into an adult.

Most of the year one would have to look for the **European newt** on land, under leaves, stones and roots, but during the breeding season it can be found in ponds, where it is easier to observe. At that time the male develops a bright crest along his back and puts on an impressive display to attract the female.

Common **snapping turtles** sometimes reach sixty pounds in weight, while the alligator snapping turtles can weigh up to 200 pounds. They should not be handled, for they have sharp and powerful hooked jaws that can inflict terrible bites.

rocks where they remain on the alert. About the only time when painted turtles and red-bellies are seen closely is when the females leave the water to lay eggs on land—sometimes a hundred feet or more from the pond.

In Canada there is a terrapin which is able to survive the hard winter conditions that regularly freeze the ponds and lakes. This is Blanding's turtle, which so closely resembles the European mud terrapin as to be easily mistaken for it by all but the expert.

Because a pond is an inviting body of water, often choked with luxuriant vegetation, it is to be expected that birds have some temporary association with it. No birds are pond inhabitants although water birds feed in it and nest along its shores. Herons wade about in the shallow areas and reed warblers nest and call loudly from the marginal rushes. A few mammals are found living in or on the banks of a pond. Water voles burrow out under the pond where their tunnels may open into the water. Bats often fly close to the water in early evening collecting midges and other insects almost as soon as they emerge from the water as matured creatures. River otters are known to stay in ponds for a while, eating newts, turtles, insects, fishes and frogs; but when hunting grows poor they migrate overland or along streams to areas where food is more plentiful. The most impressive of the aquatic mammals found in ponds are the beavers whose dam-building operations are so often responsible for the formation of ponds in some areas.

To stand beside a pond and to gaze upon its unruffled surface while trying to see into its depths is a fascinating exercise for the enthusiast. What mysteries are hidden along the underwater foliage and what a variety of little dramas are enacted beneath that placid exterior! Only very occasionally will any facet of the teeming life be revealed to the observer on the bank; perhaps the leaping of a fish as it tries to capture a fly above the water; the surfacing of an air-breathing creature replenishing its oxygen supply; or the emergence of an adult insect from its aquatic pupal case. Such events give little indication of the complex multitude of life forms competing with one another in an endless struggle for existence within their liquid environment.

To be able to study the habits and structures of these water dwellers, we have to transfer them to small containers where they can be closely examined. Some enthusiasts may wish to take their specimens home to view them at leisure while others may not find this convenient. In either case, vessels in which to house the captives will be needed. Glass or clear plastic containers are to be preferred. For those creatures which crawl or live upon the pond bottom, white bowls or dishes are ideal. If specimens are to be examined in the field at the pondside, the size of the container can be limited for ease of transport. If, however, the specimens are to be transported, cans may be used and the final vessels will need to be larger if it is intended to keep the creatures alive for any length of time. Glass-sided aquaria are recommended in this case.

The equipment for collecting specimens need not be complicated or costly. It can consist of a fine mesh net, rather large, a small net and an oblong or square tin box fixed to a stout stick for scraping snails from the banks and bottom of the pond. For gathering underwater plants growing at some distance from the pondside, a large, three-pronged hook secured to the end of a long length of strong cord is useful and can be thrown out into the pond, allowed to sink and then dragged ashore. When lifted from the water such clumps should be quickly placed in or above a large dish or bowl so that the numerous creatures along the foliage are captured for study.

Any specimens kept at home for study should be returned to their home waters when once they have served their purpose; immature

(bottom left)
With its long, sleek body, partly-webbed feet and short, dense fur, the **otter** is well-equipped for a life in water. At times it may stay in ponds, feeding on a diet of fishes, newts, turtles, frogs and insects, but it will seek food supplies elsewhere when the pond's stock begins to run out. Clumsy on land, it dives well and swims with graceful, snakelike movements.

(bottom right)
Many ponds owe their existence to the dam-building operations of **beavers.** These well-known mammals have webbed hind feet, and their flat, paddlelike tails, which aid them in swimming, can be slapped on the water to signal danger. Their diet is mainly made up of the bark and young shoots of certain trees, supplemented by other vegetable matter.

animals can be kept so that their development to the adult form can be observed—but then the mature forms should be released somewhere close to their place of origin. Many creatures in a variety of localities throughout the world are becoming rareties, and over-enthusiastic collecting by students of nature can add to the depredation of such species. Well-intentioned liberation of captured specimens in the wrong area, too, should be avoided.

Photographing Pond Life Specimens

FORMERLY, NATURE STUDENTS made a practice of preserving specimens in spirits or mounted in specimen cases, but this easily develops into a collecting mania to the detriment of the preferred species. If the amateur naturalist is also an amateur photographer then he has at his command an almost ideal means of keeping permanent records of what he finds particularly interesting and he will greatly increase his knowledge of the habits of his "sitters" in exercising his patience while trying to photograph them in characteristic attitudes. With the apparatus and film materials available today good nature photographs are within the reach of all enthusiastic students.

Every branch of natural history photography has its own particular problems—and aquatic life is no exception. The great majority of pond life forms need to be photographed while in water and this can create special lighting problems. "Awkward" reflections can often be avoided by the use of Polaroid filters—and by special care in positioning lamps or reflectors.

The orthodox rectangular aquarium is the ideal vessel for housing specimens to be photographed and high speed flash will provide the best form of lighting. For very small subjects such as hydras, gnat larvae and water fleas, quickly assembled temporary containers may be made from two sheets of glass, two strong clips and a length of half-inch-diameter rubber tubing or elastic. The tubing is placed between the glass sheets so that it forms a letter "U" and the clips are then used to clamp the glasses together at each end, sandwiching the tubing. Water is then poured into the "U"-shaped compartment into which the specimens are later introduced. This narrow little aquarium is then propped against suitable supports (two pieces of block) with the desired background sheet placed behind it. The restricted thickness of this container will ensure that the small specimens will not be able to swim out of focus when once the camera lens has been critically focused at the short range necessary for small life study.

Complete sequences can be made of such occurrences as the emergence of a transformed dragonfly, the spawning habits of fish, the building of a water spider's diving bell or the feeding habits of the hydra. The resulting pictures can be studied at leisure and will often reveal many details that may have been missed during visual observance of

The popular **ornamental goldfish** of garden pond and home aquarium was specially bred from the wild goldfish, a rather dull brownish fish also known as cruscian carp, johnny carp or mabuna.

the same events. Moreover, it is not uncommon for minor discoveries to be made in this manner; and the photographic evidence has more than once contradicted what has been believed for many years as a result of testimony based on visual observations made long ago.

So we come to the end of this brief encounter with a pond, its plants and its animal inhabitants. Many books have been written on aquatic biology and hydrology and most of them describe ponds rather fully; but no matter how searching the description, or how detailed the study, *your* pond is a place unique in itself. Go and find it if you have never been there—it cannot be far away. Even if it is no more than a large seasonal puddle that disappears in rainless periods it is likely to contain an infinite variety of living things that go into dust as seeds and spores and cysts until water returns once again. Frogs and turtles will climb out of burrows where they have survived the summer heat and aquatic plants will bloom. Of course, most ponds remain full throughout the year and, winter or summer, support vast populations of living things. Many of these may belong to species about which knowledge is still incomplete. The casual observer and the amateur biologist can do much to further knowledge if he will watch closely and record his findings accurately and fully. Seasonal cycles of life and the succession of organisms following each other, each achieving prominence and then dying off, can be observed and described by anyone with sufficient interest. Habits of animals during breeding days or their methods of finding food make rewarding studies. Food chains and food webs in graph or chart form serve to indicate the complex inter-relationships of plants and animals. Comparative studies of various ponds can help to show the effect of differences of environment upon populations and so on; only a limited imagination will quickly exhaust the possibilities for enjoyable and informative studies of a pond. Obtain a handbook or two on aquatic life to serve as your guides; go to your pond and take pleasure from what is really a world in miniature.

In North America, **painted turtles** are a familiar sight as they bask on rocks and logs in the warm summer sun. Their bright markings make a sharp contrast with the murky waters they inhabit.

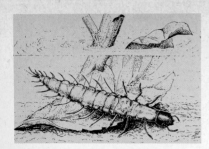

► *Animals and plants that inhabit our rivers and streams.*

Life in Flowing Waters

LEADING THROUGH THE LANDS of the earth are nature's own highways—the streams and rivers of the world, tumbling, rushing, flowing in their haste to reach the seas. Their turbulent waters carry downstream great quantities of minerals, and many plants and animals.

Flowing waters possess their own characteristic life, and biologists often are able to decide the nature of a stream by its inhabitants, perhaps without ever seeing the river itself. Physical factors such as velocity, as well as transparency and chemical conditions, can be judged from the kinds of animals occurring in streams, for these creatures reflect the conditions present in their ever-changing environment. To be sure, many forms of life are carried downstream; but for many others the stream has something of the quality of a gigantic treadmill, because they must ceaselessly strive against the tendency of the current to sweep them away from those parts of it which provide the conditions necessary for their lives.

In this chapter we shall trace a brook from its insignificant origin far inland, through its growth into a widening stream, and then into a great river bound for the sea.

Nearly every stream leads a long, full life before it loses its identity in the sea. A map can be of great help in beginning to understand these flowing waters; notice the tortuous windings of even the smallest river, and think of the stream's long journey to the sea. Then, as you glimpse a fish, frog or insect in or near the clear water, think of the many animals that are living in all those miles of river water.

If he is informed about the numbers and varieties of animals that inhabit a particular stream or river, it will often be possible for a naturalist to describe that body of flowing water, even if he has never seen it. That is because the existence of different creatures reflects the physical conditions of their water environment: swiftness, depth, clarity, chemical content, and so on. Indeed, regardless of the part of the world in which it is found, a river system will support a similar, or corresponding, animal life if conditions are comparable. This applies as much to the quiet little stream flowing sluggishly through wood or meadow as to the fast-flowing Yellowstone River, pictured above (top right).

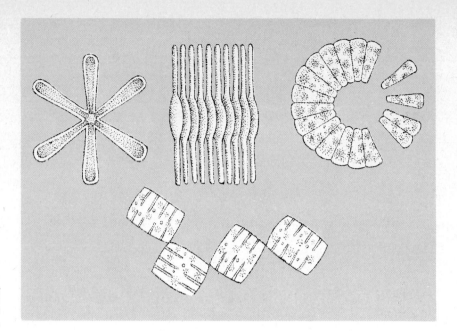

Diatoms exist in unbelievable numbers, floating near the surface in waters all over the earth. These one-celled plants are usually encased in a shell of silicon.

You will soon realize that your nearby stream is a world in itself; a world which provides one change of scene after another as you descend toward its wider reaches. Note the firm plants breaking the current; look for small, grasping insects that creep along the bottom, or for a streamlined fish as it heads into the current. Watch a water strider dart from its sheltered cove to capture a fly caught in the surface tension of the water film. Take advantage of all you can see in this brook, because there will be little chance of seeing what goes on in the churning muddy water of the lower reaches of the river. There life is hidden, and you will have to travel many miles until the clearer waters of a bay are reached and animals may be seen once more.

What starts a stream? Perhaps a heavy rain, melting snow, or an ancient glacier; or perhaps it is an upwelling of water filtered and trapped beneath layers of rock. It may start as a raging torrent, slashing down a mountainside; it may be no more than a permanently wet corner of a field.

Because many of us live where streams are likely to begin slowly, we can easily visualize this simple birth—a sprightly bubbling from a hillside spring into a small pool below, and leading off across a meadow, a tiny, clear brook.

It is pleasant to lie on the thick grass and hang your head over the cool water. On sudden impulse you may cup your hands and splash water on your face, until your skin reddens and tingles. Pebbles and sand gleam on the bottom. Here suddenly a shadow hovers for an instant as a brilliant darter swims by, intent on a small aquatic insect whose protective camouflage has enabled it to escape notice until now.

(left)
Desmids are microscopic one-celled algae made up of two symmetrical halves. There is often a narrower, constricted area between the halves, making the division quite evident.

(below)
Many streams have a **kingfisher** that either visits regularly or lives somewhere along the banks. This bright, alert bird is accustomed to patrolling flowing waters and diving after small fish that swim near the surface.

The characteristics of this clear brook are repeated many times throughout the world; although no two brooks are exactly alike there are some features which are common to all of them. The similarities account for the fact that animals and plants found in a stream in England may be quite like those living half a world away in Japan; the latter will have to combat the same forces and acquire similar food. The life in the meadow brook which we shall consider is much like the life of any other lowland brook in the northern hemisphere.

Primitive Plants

Along the shaded banks of a woodland brook small flat plants sometimes grow in profusion, plants with broad, emerald-green blades that stretch across damp rocks. These are the liverworts, primitive plants that seldom are found very far from moisture, and which often thrive in a zone of splashing and misting from a turbulent stream. Here, in the shadow of high banks and trees, the sun's rays never penetrate with such intensity as to remove, by evaporation, the abundant moisture necessary for the perpetuation of the plants.

Like the mosses which are their relatives, liverworts have a complicated life cycle. Close examination of these small plants at a certain stage in their lives will reveal tiny erect structures rising from the broad blades of each individual plant. These are the reproductive organs, some male, some female—but only a single kind to any one plant. Unlike the higher plants, the male structures do not release dusty pollen, but liberate sperm cells that swim—a fact which demands the presence of water if the sperm are to journey successfully to a nearby plant where eggs awaiting fertilization are contained within female organs. Liver-worts *must* live in an environment damp enough to provide the coating of moisture on the plant surfaces necessary for a sufficiency of sperm cells to accomplish their journey and ensure the plants' continual reproduction.

Freshwater Sponges

IT IS NOT POPULARLY KNOWN that sponges can be found in fresh waters. Those who know that sponges are animals usually associate them with the oceans; but clear-running fresh waters often support yellow, brown, or green encrusting masses that upon close inspection prove to be true sponges.

These simple, loosely organized animals can be found attached to sub-merged rocks, logs, pilings and the like. If the water flowing past them is not too swift, they develop erect finger-like projections. Freshwater sponges for the most part are small, but they have been known to form a continuous carpet of about 400 square feet in conditions especially suited to their growth.

A sponge is a primitive mass of indistinctly arranged cells, and to the casual observer it hardly seems an animate creature. But when a bit of powdered carmine, or some other non-toxic dye, is added to the water close to the sponge, it will drift into the tissues and then be expelled through conspicuous pores in the outer wall. The interior of a sponge is a labyrinth of interconnecting spaces and chambers. The walls of some of the chambers are lined with cells bearing tiny whips—flagellae—which lash the water and create the currents visible from the outerside. Water flowing into the cells not only brings with it food in the form of minute organisms, but continually replenishes the supply of oxygen; the out-going current removes carbon dioxide and other wastes from the sponge's process of living.

The green hue that is typical of some freshwater sponges is provided by the large numbers of microscopic algae embedded in their tissues. Formerly it was thought that a mutual give-and-take relationship existed between the sponge and its algae, but now it is known that the algae are taken in during the process of "feeding" and are slowly digested. Sunlight falling on the sponge may enable the algae to reproduce and become so abundant as to tint the entire mass; but in a shaded place sponges are more likely to be yellow or brown because the algae have been consumed.

A sponge with its loose, fleshy tissues needs some kind of support or framework, and it provides its own by manufacturing geometrically patterned spicules from the element silicon, together with tiny traces of water, magnesium and sodium oxides included. Although silicon may be rare in fresh waters, sponges have the ability to select it even in the smallest quantities for the construction of their skeletons. The result seems to be a haphazard supporting structure, for it consists

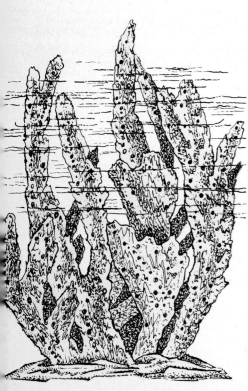

At least forty to fifty species of **fresh-water sponges** are known. They all would suffocate in still water; currents are needed to bring them their food and carry away wastes.

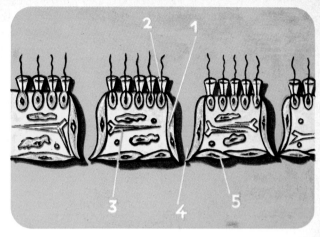

of nothing but a great mass of glasslike rods and hooks, all tangled together resembling nothing so much as the game of jackstraws. Covering the skeleton of spicules is the welding, binding tissue of living cells, with the result that a sponge is a fairly firm though shapeless animal.

During summer, small embryos of the sponges are released as a result of a primitive union of sperms and eggs. For a brief spell these embryos swim freely; then they descend and attach themselves to the bottom where they grow into a new sponge. In preparation for winter, however, another development takes place. Bits of a sponge's tissue become surrounded by a highly resistant covering of dead outer layer and spicules. This "spore" survives through the most difficult cold months, and early in the spring splits open to allow new growth to commence. At times in the fall, rocks and logs upon which sponges have grown through the summer are covered with these resting bodies, or *gemmules*.

(top left)
Most of the **sponges** that live in fresh water are small. They grow on submerged rocks and logs, projecting branches outward if the water current is not too strong.

(top right)
The minute organisms that the sponge consumes for food enter it in the water that flows through the inhaling pores (4) between the binding outer cells (1, 5). With the water, oxygen is also brought into the sponge. When the water leaves, it takes carbon dioxide and other wastes with it. A skeleton of spicules (3) made from silicon gives support to the tissues. In some of the chambers the walls are lined with tiny whips (2) that lash the water, creating the currents necessary to move it out through the pores.

Tiny Clams

Pill clams, or fingernail clams as some related forms are called, can be found in small creeks and brooks, but only by those who are sharp-eyed and willing to sift through bottom sand. They are true clams, but only a fraction of an inch across—and their hue is likely to be much the same as that of the pebbles among which they live.

If a few pill clams are found and placed in a small aquarium, they may produce perfectly formed young—although this will not be apparent without a magnifying lens, because they are no larger than pin-heads. Actually, the young are retained within the parent's body until they are able to live by themselves. Sometimes this means that by the time they are thrown out into the world, they are nearly a third as large as their parents. You may wonder, and rightly so, how they all fitted within the parent shell. The fact that the adult possesses a high-arched shell indicates that there is more space within it than might be suspected.

Pill clams are sought and eaten by many fishes. Although we cannot always find the small mollusks, they must exist in large numbers, for some fishes' stomachs have been found to be packed with their tiny shells.

Valuable Shrimps

ONE OF THE MOST UNIVERSALLY DISTRIBUTED ANIMALS in brooks and streams is the scud, and other scuds live in rivers, bays and oceans. This little shrimp is one of nature's most successful forms of life, and wherever it is found it usually is present in huge numbers. I have scraped river buoys and in a short time packed a quart bottle solid with scuds, and during springtime biologists have gathered as many as 10,000 of these animals in less than a square yard!

All over the world the scud is one of the most important food animals to be found in streams; nearly all fishes, as well as many birds, insects and amphibians, eat it. Female scuds reproduce rapidly and produce approximately fifty well-developed young which have been allowed to grow in a brood pouch. Once free, the young eat plant material, minute animals and decaying matter.

Scuds are active at any time, but their activity increases at night. They often crawl about the bottom scavenging for food, and easily rise to the surface or to an aquatic plant. They swim with a skittering motion, and frequently turn over on their sides or even upside down. You can find them in large numbers most easily by turning over submerged stones. Many of them blend with their background, but there are some which contrast violently with the stream bottom, and this makes them easy to see.

A Spider that Takes to Water

THE LARGE, COMMON FISHER SPIDER which lurks along the shores of brooks is one of the most fascinating beasts of prey to be found anywhere. It is a big, handsome spider whose furry body is often strikingly marked, and it has eight staring eyes arranged around the front of its head. Despite its size, its weight is so evenly and lightly distributed on its eight legs that it can run across the surface film of water to grasp and paralyze a struggling insect caught in mid-stream. The fisher spider is not limited to life above the water, and when danger threatens it has a trick which insures its safety. If you watch a fisher resting on a leaf in a quiet cove of the brook, and draw near slowly, you will be likely to find that the spider is suddenly no longer visible. Investigation will show that it has ducked under the leaf and is waiting for you to leave. While submerged, it breathes from a thin film of silvery air trapped in the long hairs of its body. Fisher spiders have been known to remain underwater for three-quarters of an hour.

Fisher spiders are voracious hunters and capture their aquatic prey

The **water-lily leaf beetle** lays its eggs on floating leaves; when they hatch, the larvae drop down through the water and attach themselves to stems. Remarkably, by breaking into the air-filled stems, they can breathe air three or four feet underwater.

Often found lurking along the banks of brooks and streams, the furry **fisher spider** is only semi-aquatic. However, it can run across open water without breaking the surface film when it needs to escape danger or to attack its prey, and it can remain underwater for forty-five minutes or more. In this picture a female is carrying her egg sac.

with a great deal of skill. One of the best methods of finding and studying these large spiders is to stalk them at night, when they are most active. In the beam of a powerful flashlight, their eyes reflect light with a green brilliance. The sight is unlikely to be forgotten; they can be seen from a great distance along the stream bank. If you learn how to do this, take out a friend at night and tell him you see a large spider in the flashlight beam twenty feet away. He won't believe you until you walk over and prove your statement.

Aquatic Insects

SOME NATURALISTS HAVE TAKEN PLEASURE in saying that this is not the "Age of Man" but the "Age of Insects". Such statements provoke arguments, and with good reason, but one point cannot be denied: insects inhabit the earth more completely than we do. Take our river for example. Without the assistance of man-made devices, what can we do other than to swim along the shore? Insects, on the other hand, hover above it, burrow beneath it, swim through it and float upon it. They breathe air through long "snorkel" tubes, or take oxygen directly from the water through gills. They are present at the birth of the river in a spring pool; they live in the widening river stream; some of them are able to live even in stretches which are most polluted by waste products. They live offshore, in bays, and some even live on the ocean surface far out from land. They may live in rivers their whole lives, being as streamlined and as successful swimmers as fish. For others, life in a brook represents only a brief stage of their development. Different species eat aquatic vegetation, other animals, or organic matter lying on the bottom. The varieties of insects and variations in their habits, even of those within a river, are unending.

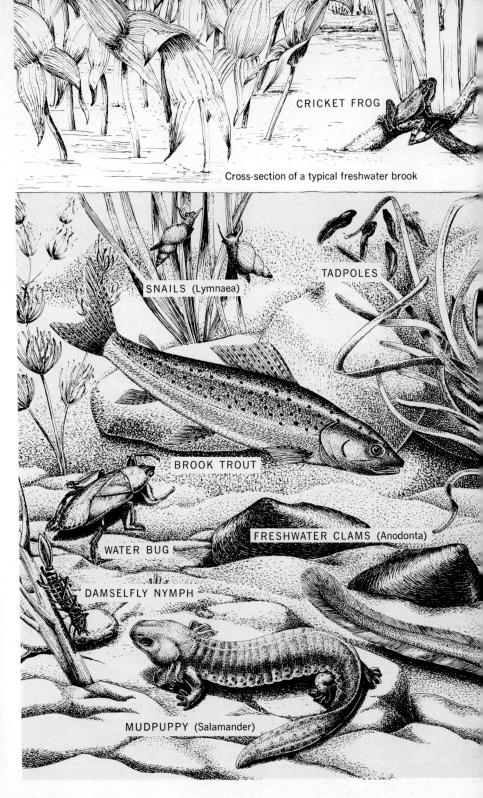

CRICKET FROG

Cross-section of a typical freshwater brook

SNAILS (Lymnaea)

TADPOLES

BROOK TROUT

FRESHWATER CLAMS (Anodonta)

WATER BUG

DAMSELFLY NYMPH

MUDPUPPY (Salamander)

With front legs adapted for seizing prey, the **giant water bug** feeds on insects and other small animals. When the eggs are laid, they are glued to the back of the male, giving him an odd appearance in midsummer.

DRAGONFLY

PAINTED TURTLE

BROOK STICKLEBACK

FRESHWATER CRAYFISH

DIVING BEETLE

AMERICAN EEL

An insect fisherman, the **larva of the caddis fly** spins a web facing into the current above its tubular "house." It ventures out upon occasion to collect the food that has been caught in the silken net. Almost covered with gills on its undersurface, it lives in well-aerated water.

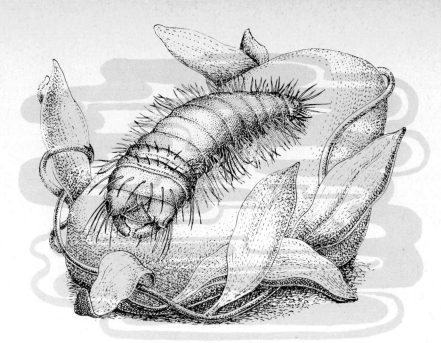

Unusual among moths, the **caterpillar of the Elophila moth** lives in swift waters and even weaves a silken pupal case underwater. It breathes through double rows of gills along its body.

(above)
While some **mayfly nymphs** range freely through rapid streams, the species pictured here burrows in soft banks along the water's edge, constructing a U-shaped tube. It brings oxygen and plant food into its burrow by fanning its gills, so that a constant current enters and leaves. Adult mayflies, often present in huge swarms near water, have delicate, gauzelike wings.

Brooks contain many surprises, but none greater than an insect fisherman—the caddis fly larva that constructs a conical silken net in the swiftest regions of a stream. Opening from the downstream tip of the net there is a tubular case made from scraps of vegetable matter or sand grains; in this lair the larva rests securely. At frequent intervals it emerges halfway from the case and busily gathers the bits of animal and plant matter that have been caught in the net.

Adult caddis flies are large-winged insects, capable of rapid flight. As is the case with all mature insects, they draw in air through a system of air tubes, or tracheae, that branch through their bodies. The larvae, on the other hand, cannot rise to the surface of a rapid stream to take in air; they have to get their oxygen from the well-aerated water surrounding them. To allow adequate diffusion of this gas to maintain their high level of bodily activity, there are pairs of branched gills arising from nearly all the abdominal segments. Oxygen diffuses into the air-tubes that lie just beneath the surface of the gills—and, of course, carbon dioxide, a waste gas, passes out. In this way a caddis fly larva spends its entire immature existence—a period of a year—in its secure house which opens directly upon an efficient and well-constructed net.

Mayflies by the Million

IN LAKE REGIONS, and more locally around ponds and streams, delicate flying insects of a particular kind are found in vast swarms that make it impossible to ignore them; they may even halt traffic by piling up along the roads in immense numbers, rendering the surface slippery and dangerous. These are the mayflies, and accounts of their swarms appear from time to time in newspapers.

Mayfly nymphs, adapted either to a wandering or a burrowing

existence, can be found in ponds and lakes as well as in running waters. One species is a burrowing form found in the soft bottom of a slow stream. In effect, these nymphs are miniature moles and use legs, mouth parts and body movements to construct U-shaped tubes in the mud. Seepage keeps the tubes flooded; but because the exchange of water is slow, the constant demand for oxygen in the water presents something of a problem. The nymph fans its large, branched gills in such a fashion that a constant current enters the tube, bringing with it oxygen and bits of plant food, and carrying away waste material as it leaves the other end.

Another immature aquatic insect that lives in fast-flowing water is the stonefly nymph. This spread-legged creature crawls across rock surfaces in search of the other aquatic insects that form its food. Its gills, not as conspicuous as in some of the other forms described here, can be re-tracted or extended as the need arises. If the stonefly nymph finds itself in fairly still water, it will pump its body up and down to create a current that will make it impossible for stale water to accumulate.

Adult stoneflies emerge late in the year, perhaps even in winter, which means a short life span—short at least in the adult stage, al-though the nymphs may live for two or three years.

Perfect Streamlining

NOT MANY ADULT BEETLES are associated with the swiftest streams, but riffle beetles are an exception. They seem to prefer the most turbulent and rapid brooks. They do not swim, but creep about along the bottom, or cling to submerged rocks and pebbles in search of food—and they emerge frequently, not only to breathe, but to rest and crawl along the banks. Like many other adult aquatic insects, when submerging they take down a supply of air trapped in a dense coating of hair, which enables them to remain under the surface for long periods of time.

The larva of a riffle beetle is a curious and unusual animal, known as a water penny; it is almost perfectly streamlined, and with the con-certed effect of both grasping legs and a suction disk created by the margin of the entire body, it clings to rocks in the most rapid currents. The first time you see a water penny it may remind you of limpets, or possibly of the ancient trilobites; but if you remove one carefully and turn it over, its six pairs of legs, mouth parts and five pairs of highly branched gills will be quite obvious, and clearly identify the animal as an insect adapted to life in the water.

Of all the predatory aquatic insects, none is more dangerous to other dwellers of slow streams than the diving beetle. In this small but ferocious creature, both the larval stage and the adult are carnivorous and both live in water. If you wish to find them in brooks, look along the banks in submerged vegetation, where they have objects to grasp and rest upon. From here the adult diving beetles sally forth to

(below)
Stonefly nymphs are found in the swiftest streams—even around water-falls—where there is an abundance of dissolved oxygen. This one, a North American green-winged stonefly, usually lives in cold, rocky brooks.

(bottom)
A curious insect adapted to life in streams, the symmetrical, streamlined **water penny** is the larva of a riffle beetle. The margin of the water penny's body serves as a suction disc that enables it to hold on to stones in the swiftest currents, and oxygen is drawn from the water through gills on the underside of the animal.

capture dragonfly nymphs, small fishes and tadpoles—all of which are their natural prey. They move rapidly and powerfully with oarlike hind legs.

Diving beetles breathe air as do all adult insects, and they accomplish this by hanging just below the surface of the water where they draw air into chambers beneath the wing covers. In the winter when their rate of breathing is slowed, they hibernate successfully on the brook bottom.

Diving beetles sometimes take wing and fly from one body of water to another, and if the migration takes place at night they may be attracted to lights and buzz about in noisy confusion. They are able to make sounds intentionally, too, by rubbing their wing covers or legs against their abdomens.

Although diving beetle larvae are very different from the adults in appearance, they are every bit as fierce. They are long, cigar-shaped animals that live on the bottom of slow brooks and wait for their prey to come near them. Their heads are fitted with powerful, grooved, sickle-shaped jaws. Digestive fluids flow through the grooves into the body of the victim; then it is sucked back into the mouth along the same grooves in the form of a partially pre-digested meal. Diving beetle larvae are so fierce in their habits that they are known as "water tigers".

Dwellers of the Surface Film

I N A RAPID BROOK the surface is fractured and rippled so constantly that it cannot support plants and animals, but where the velocity slows and the stream's surface is smoothed, various forms of life take residence upon it, or just under it. Perhaps the most common surface dweller is that active, spindle-legged insect, the water strider.

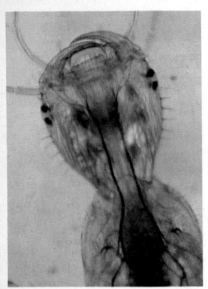

(above)
The sharp, sickle-shaped jaws of a
diving beetle larva hold the unlucky
victim caught in their grip. Then a
digestive fluid enters the victim's body
through channels in the jaws, dissolving
the insides so that they can be
sucked out.

(right)
Backswimmers spend a lot of time
hanging upside-down from the surface
film, breathing through tubes in the
tail. They are most noticeable, however,
when they dive to the bottom,
sculling themselves along with their
long hind legs.

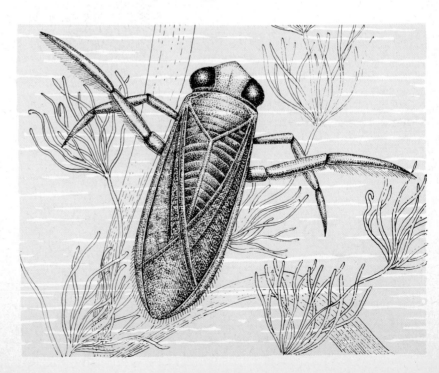

Water striders usually exist in large congregations either upon the surface or on shaded rocks. A water strider on land is a clumsy creature, but it can cover distances on the water with great rapidity. At times striders can be seen heading upstream at the same speed as the water velocity, thereby just maintaining their position on the flowing water as though they were on a tread mill. These insects are predators, and attack many small stream dwellers.

Predatory Insects

No STREAM IS COMPLETE without its fast-darting dragonflies and its brilliant, hovering damselflies. The two are much the same, although their flying habits and their dissimilar hues may suggest they are very different creatures. Each is an active predator, both are basically alike in structure, and all members of the group are tied to an aquatic environment because, as nymphs, they must develop stages under water.

Damselfly nymphs have three flat gills rising from the tail region into which tubular tracheae extend. They lack obvious gills, but have a spacious abdominal chamber into which water is drawn and there deprived of its oxygen. The adaptations of these nymphs to watery environments are many—some are streamlined, some burrow, some crawl about, and some sprawl on the bottom.

The mouth parts of damselfly and dragonfly nymphs are extremely curious. When either attacks its victim, the whole body lunges forward and, simultaneously, a hinged, two-jawed mouth appendage unfolds and shoots out far ahead of the creature. There it fastens on the prey, returns to its former position, and the food is thrust against the true jaws which crush it, and tear it apart. Thorough chewing is completed further down the digestive tract in a gizzard which has in it heavy toothed ridges. The whole process of attack is over so quickly that it must be carefully observed many times before the sequence of events becomes clear.

When the nymph is ready for transformation into an adult—after per-

(top left)
Long and cigar-shaped, the **larva of the diving beetle** is a fiercely active predator, just like the adult form. This seems to be its mode of life during the summer. Its rate of breathing slows in the winter, when it hibernates at the bottom and its activities come to a halt. Diving beetles are also known as "water tigers."

(top center)
A master of the art of treading lightly, the **water strider** spends its life standing on or running across the fragile surface film of the water.

(top right)
Adult **diving beetles** swim rapidly and powerfully through the water in search of their elusive prey. Sometimes they take wing and fly off to another body of water.

A prized and highly regarded species, the **brook trout** lives in clear, rapid streams. When spawning, it seeks even swifter streams with gravel bottoms. After sweeping out a hole with her tail, the female deposits the eggs, which are fertilized by the male. Then she covers them with sand and gravel, the male standing guard until she has finished.

haps three or four years of aquatic development—it crawls from the water upon a stem or rock exposed to the air. Then a longitudinal split in the tough outer skeleton appears and gradually the body, head, legs and wings, and finally the abdomen, are brought forth. The new adult cannot fly until its newly exposed exoskeleton and wings have been dried out thoroughly. The cast-off, shell-like skins of nymphs are sometimes very common along the banks of streams, and people often have no idea what they are, or what animal has emerged from them.

Fishes of the Brook

BROOKS DO NOT SUPPORT many species of fishes, but those which are found usually are adapted for this specialized environment. There is one relative of the perch family which is seldom found in any habitat other than a brook or stream. It is the darter, and its body and habits are peculiarly suited to life in flowing water.

Darters have no "swim bladder"—that internal organ of buoyancy which enables most fishes to remain suspended in water with little or no effort; so they are heavier than water and sink to the bottom. Because they must live on the bottom, their fins are adapted to creeping and skipping along and are almost like feeble, finny legs.

These animals are interesting to watch while feeding, and always puzzle their observers because, although they never quite seem to reach the prey they are stalking, the victim seldom escapes! There is a simple solution to the mystery: the darter leaps forward just short of the insect or shrimp, opens its mouth and then simply *sucks in its prey*.

Darters live in cool brooks and cannot survive in home aquaria. They should not be removed from streams, but many pleasant hours can be spent watching their activities in clear water.

The shiner is another inhabitant of cool streams and rivers, but is not likely to be found so far upstream as the darter. It is a larger fish, and is sometimes caught by fishermen when it reaches a length of eight or ten inches; but this size is rare.

The redfin shiner assumes a gaudy appearance in the spring during its breeding season. The fins of the male become a vivid scarlet that gradually fades during the summer and finally disappears with the coming of cold weather. Visitors to streams in the springtime can occasionally enjoy an unusual sight when, during spawning, large numbers of shiners gather in flashing, seething masses which break the surface of the water again and again.

Dangers in the Stream

Life is a precarious matter for nearly all brook and stream animals, and the fastest fish is not always safe from harm. Fishes are caught by man and are sought as food by animals which lie in wait for them in the water, above it, or along the shore; and neither great speed nor wariness can save a fish from the effects of chemical pollution and artificially changed temperature conditions. How is it they continue to survive?

Nearly all creatures possess techniques which help their species to survive, but special methods of survival are needed for those which live in the world of brooks and streams. First, animals living in flowing water must combat the current to keep from being swept downstream. This

(left)
Although fish do most of their feeding underwater, some kinds are alert to the presence of living food beyond the confines of a stream. A **brook trout can leap several feet** to capture a moth flying above the water.

(below)
A member of the carp family, the **shiner** lives in cool streams and rivers. The shimmering body of one species—the common shiner—can be seen in almost every brook in the eastern part of the United States.

Marsh ducks, on the way north to their breeding grounds, stop to rest at a fresh-water pond. A male shoveler and mallard rest and preen (lower right) as a male cinnamon teal flies overhead. In the center foreground, a male American widgeon, or baldpate, and a male hooded merganser share a mat of dead reeds. Any relatively sheltered body of fresh water with a food supply serves as a lifesaver for these ducks on their arduous spring and fall migrations (provided, of course, that it is not polluted with oil slicks, in which case it can become a death trap).

they may accomplish with sprawling, grasping legs as seen in the nymphs of the dragonfly, damselfly and stonefly. Others may construct burrows or even "houses" as do the larvae of midges, caddis flies and hellgrammites. Some are firmly rooted—the sponge, for example—but others are so perfectly streamlined that they move about easily even in the swiftest water. The water penny is perhaps one of the most efficiently streamlined animals in the entire brook.

Two other methods of survival in streams concern reproduction. One method is to produce enough young to make sure that not all will be eaten or succumb in other ways; another is to protect the young during early growth in some fashion. The brook trout is an excellent example of a creature that uses both of these methods of insurance.

Brook trout live in clear, rapid brooks. In the autumn, when the urge to spawn comes upon them, they seek even more rapid streams where a gravel bottom is present. There the female swims down to the bottom, lies on her side and waves her tail vigorously. This sweeps out a depression in the gravel, and a "nest" is formed. After the eggs have been laid and fertilized, she employs similar means to cover the eggs with sand and gravel. During all this work, the male stands guard and drives off any intruders, particularly other male trout attempting to claim the female. Although a trout does not lay nearly as many eggs as some fishes do, it will deposit over a thousand eggs during its breeding season.

The eggs develop slowly under protecting pebbles and sand. Light and enemies are kept out, but the necessary oxygen in the water above diffuses down, making it possible for the eggs to "breathe" and develop. Each egg contains one developing embryo and a supply of yolk. After hatching the embryo looks like a tiny pot-bellied fish. Some other species of fishes actually do swim about in this condition, living on the enclosed yolk until it is completely consumed. The trout, however, emerges from its hiding place only when fully formed. Development depends upon the temperature, and if the eggs have been laid in the late autumn, the young fish probably will not emerge until the following spring, when they will be more active—and food plentiful.

Despite such instinctive protection given to the young by the adults, most of the thousands that emerge in the spring will never live more than a few days; they will fall prey to the many hungry predators that abound in and near the brook at this time of the year. Furthermore, if the character of the stream becomes much changed, whether through natural or man-made causes, game fishes may not reproduce sufficiently to maintain their numbers.

Aquatic Snakes

O F THE WATER SNAKES often associated with brooks, the queen snake is one of the most attractive. This slender animal may exist in considerable numbers without anyone's knowing it; for the queen

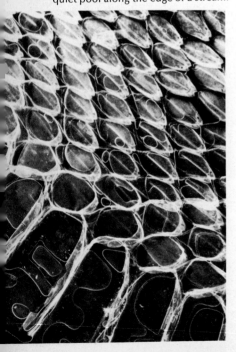

A snake periodically sheds its skin. In this picture, the **skin of a water snake** is seen drifting over the surface of a quiet pool along the edge of a stream.

snake is a timid and retiring creature that lies well hidden along the banks of streams, usually under flat rocks along the water's edge, or in burrows excavated by other animals in the stream bank. When queen snakes are discovered and frightened, they dive into the water at once and take refuge in the bottom mud where they remain for a considerable period. They are good swimmers, and hard to catch in the water.

Wherever queen snakes are present crayfish can also be expected, since —apart from an occasional frog or fish—these freshwater crustaceans are their only food. Queen snakes are harmless and need not be feared, even if in some localities they are called "moccasins". The true water moccasin is a southern aquatic snake, very poisonous, and quite different from the non-poisonous group known as water snakes, of which the queen snake is a member. But anyone who lives where true water moccasins are known to exist will wisely leave all aquatic snakes strictly alone, for disastrous errors in identification have been known to occur.

The happy chatter of a brook is soon lost when it joins a larger, slower stream. Here the aquatic life becomes more complex and varied. Larger, more powerful fishes seek a greater abundance of food; turtles bask on the shore ready to slip into the current at the least disturbance. A faint "plop" tells us a frog has leaped to safety. Thousands of smaller creatures such as insects construct elaborate devices to insure protection and a continuing supply of food. In five minutes of looking about, we know that the infancy of the river is past and that it is growing up.

One of the few live animals ever used to treat humans for disease, **leeches** are common inhabitants of the sheltered backwaters of streams and ponds. While some animals are difficult to catch, these may be collected by accident. They can drink twice their weight in blood if they get a chance, but they can last a year or more between meals.

The "Good" of an Animal

WHEN YOU WALK ALONG THE BANK of a stream and see small aquatic animals busy in their everyday activity, do not ask, "Well, what *good* are they?" A little thought and study will show you that they, as do all creatures, occupy important places in the natural world; their value is not less real for being one which has no meaning in terms of money. Every living community resembles a chain; the animals and plants are the links, and a stream community is no exception. The welfare of each animal living in a stream is linked to the availability and number of organisms upon which it feeds. Furthermore, its survival depends upon how well it escapes predators that seek it for nourishment. Take away an animal (or link), and the whole structure of the community may be changed.

Crawdads, crayfish, crawfish . . . what do you call the large freshwater crustaceans that inhabit many inland waters? If I call them crayfish and you call them by another name, let us agree that we are referring to the same kind of animal. In rivers, streams and brooks, as well as in ponds and lakes, crayfish live in large numbers. In some streams of the United States collectors have obtained over 1,000 pounds of crayfish per acre of water, and as each one is seldom much more than five inches in length, this means a great many were collected.

(above)
This cutaway drawing of a **crayfish** shows the stomach, the heart and the blood vessels. The mobile eyes are on stalks, and there are two pairs of antennae—the long ones are feelers and the shorter pair have the hearing organ at their base. The tail can be doubled up underneath when the crayfish moves backward quickly.

(above right)
Chimney crayfish build long tunnels back into the shore, ending them high on the bank in a tube, or chimney, formed by mud pellets. In these tunnels the crayfish hide from predators, appearing at the opening only at night.

Crayfish live on the bottom of streams where they walk about slowly sifting through the sediment. They are true scavengers, although they will also eat fresh vegetation. Fed properly with bits of fresh meat, they make satisfactory aquarium pets and you will find the complicated action of their limbs and other appendages makes them fascinating creatures to watch. Crayfish are able to detect food by touch and smell, both senses being located in the long antennae. The large claws then grasp a morsel and pass it to smaller appendages near the mouth which promptly tear it apart; the jaws themselves, which are not easily visible, give a final mincing to the food before it is swallowed.

If you happen to live near a stream in which crayfish can be found, do not expect to see them crawling about; they usually retire under stones and into burrows during daytime. Lifting stones along the bottom may reveal a few; but be prepared to grab. When alarmed, crayfish quickly double their tails under them and shoot backward. Several strokes of this kind in quick succession will soon put one far beyond your reach.

Along the banks of streams you may come across a neat pile of mud pellets, each with a central hole. These are the "chimneys" of the burrowing crayfish. This species seldom ventures into the open stream itself, but hides deep in its tunnels which will have to be completely dug out before you can hope to capture a specimen. The chimney crayfish resembles a miniature lobster—and, often, it has a brightly tinted carapace. The animal brings up mud from wherever it is excavating, and places it in pellets about the entrance of the burrow. This is done only at night. The tunnels themselves are somewhat branched, and may be enlarged to form small chambers in which the animal rests.

Other crayfish live more freely, and wander about in the bottom

One of the fiercest small predators of moving streams is the **hellgrammite,** the larva of the dobson fly. Its large, powerful jaws are capable of tearing apart not only other aquatic insects but small fish and eels as well. Sometimes swimming with a waving motion of its body, it more often walks over the bottom, holding on tightly when the current is strong.

sediment. They keep within a certain territory, and are apt to have some customary resting place of their own to which they usually return.

A female crayfish is a good mother by instinct. Before the eggs are laid, she secretes a gluelike substance on her abdomen. For security, the fertilized eggs are then attached to the abdomen by short stalks. She keeps them supplied with fresh, clean water by slow movements of her abdominal appendages. Several weeks pass before the eggs hatch out into very small crayfish which hang on tightly to the fanning append-ages. Not until growing crayfish have shed their hard outer skin three times will they be large enough to fend for themselves and leave their mother for good.

Young Predators

THE STREAM IS A WORLD largely populated with immature insects; whether they are called "larvae" or "nymphs" depends upon their type of life cycle. With insects such as butterflies and moths, the larvae hatch from eggs, grow and then rest in a cocoon, or pupal stage. Others, as for example grasshoppers, hatch from eggs as nymphs which grow directly into adults with no resting stage.

One of the most ferocious of all water-dwelling larvae is the hell-grammite, which possesses large "rock-crusher" jaws capable of snaring not only other aquatic insects that are its usual food, but small fish and young eels as well. Hellgrammites live in both swift brooks and slower streams. They can swim by waving their bodies back and forth, but usually move about by walking along the bottom which they can grasp tightly even in a swift current. It is natural that we should know more of the larvae of these insects than of the adults; the larval stage may account for two or three years—but "grown-up" life is all over in a matter of days. Nevertheless, in that short time the adults, as large flying insects, ensure the future of their kind by laying several thousand eggs on shoreline vegetation. As soon as the eggs hatch, the larvae fall into the water below and stake their ferocious claim to existence.

If the stream is carpeted with vegetation, there is a good chance that water boatmen will be living there in large numbers. These small insects dart about beneath the surface by means of their long, oarlike third pair of legs. The second pair of legs is used only when the animal rests on a submerged plant; the rest of the time this pair is folded back flat against the body. Their first legs are not used as "legs" at all—but as organs for sweeping food into the mouth.

When submerged, water boatmen carry air as an air film that covers much of their bodies and causes them to glisten. Although the hues of boatmen are usually quite striking if seen against a dull background, they normally move around in areas where they blend fairly well with their surroundings. They are strong fliers and are able to take off directly from the water, and quite commonly desert one stream for another.

Noisemakers

IT MIGHT SEEM STRANGE that water insects should make noises; but water boatmen are able to "chirp" by rubbing their front legs against a scraper on the sides of their heads. Only the males can do this —and only during the breeding season.

Other noisy animals—and ones that produce far louder and more familiar calls—are the frogs. Although many frogs spend much of their time on the marshy banks of a stream—and others travel far across dry land—all must return to an aquatic environment to mate and lay their eggs. During spring, in quiet pools along the margins of a lowland stream, great masses of frogs' eggs can be seen in the shallow water. Each egg is suspended in a gelatinous substance. Within a day or two enough change has taken place to see the beginnings of a head and tail, and soon after this development the tiny immature tadpoles break free and commence an existence of their own. At first they feed upon stored yolk, but before long they begin to forage for themselves among the water plants. The intricate and wonderful transformation of tadpole to frog has been described many times, and although it is one of the most remarkable changes that take place in nature, it can be seen very easily by anyone who is prepared to take even the slightest amount of trouble.

A similar life cycle is found in another group of amphibians, the salamanders. Their eggs, too, are deposited in protecting gelatinous masses; but the young that later emerge closely resemble the parents except for the possession of a pair of branched, feathery gills that protrude from either side of the head. As the transformation toward a terrestrial way of life progresses, these gills become absorbed and eventually disappear.

A true amphibian, the **frog** may spend much of its life on land, but it must return to the water to breed. When it is preparing to go ashore it will first surface, with its body submerged and only its eyes exposed, to see if it is safe to come out.

(left)
Known as the **plastron,** the hard shell on the underside of a turtle is formed from fused plates. It may virtually cover the bottom surface of the reptile, as in the case of this fresh-water turtle, or—as in snapping turtles— it may be quite small and protect only a limited area.

(below)
Almost totally aquatic, **snapping turtles** rarely venture on land. When they do, it is usually to prowl the land for food. Ferocious predators, they have a lightning-fast thrust that can snap up fish, frogs, small water birds and other animals, including fast-moving creatures.

Of course there are exceptions to all rules that concern living things, and this is particularly true with frogs and salamanders; some frogs breed only in icy ponds; some salamanders never lose their external gills; and other salamanders lay their eggs in rotten logs.

Actually most animals, regardless of what they are, that live in brooks and streams deposit their eggs there too. Only a few aquatic creatures —turtles, water snakes and a few insects—seek dry land on which to lay eggs. Fishes, mollusks, most aquatic insects and amphibians place their eggs in the water, either on the bottom or on vegetation and stones.

In many areas the surface of a meandering meadow stream is broken frequently by a triangular head that gazes about briefly, and then ducks back to watery depths. To the initiated, this means the presence of a turtle; but which particular turtle even the experts will find difficult to tell. One North American species, common to Atlantic Coast lowland streams and tidal creeks, is the eastern snapper; another, farther to the west in the Mississippi drainage, is the huge alligator snapper. These animals are about as aquatic as any freshwater turtles in the world, and only seldom venture on land. They are powerful and ferocious predators, and possess a lightning-fast thrust. Not only do they account for aquatic victims such as fishes and frogs and the like, but also for water birds and small mammals that venture too close to the water's edge.

River Scene

By the time a large river is reached, we are conscious of the solemn grandeur and power exhibited by the ceaseless flow of the mighty stream. It surges forward in the peak of its life, mature and independent, and we find it hard to believe that this great body of water owes its existence to the tiny brooks from which we have recently come.

Along the shore there is little to be seen in the water, because the river is opaque and brownish, owing to the enormous amounts of suspended matter—soil and decayed vegetation swept downstream from the banks and adjoining fields. Not until the flow of the river slows almost to a halt, in the vicinity of a dam or a deep natural pool, will the finer material become sediment, and the water clear once more. A few small fishes dash about in shallow water, and an occasional turtle may thrust its head above the surface to take a breath; but living creatures are mostly well hidden by the muddy waters.

Out in a boat, large swirls are evident in the cloudy water, and these evoke many a question—and many a wrongly guessed answer. Probably none of the guesses takes account of one of the possible causes—a great river sturgeon, groping and rooting through the bottom sediment. These large fishes are seldom seen and rarely caught nowadays, although they are good eating and can provide delicious caviar. Some sturgeons, such as the giants found in the Columbia River in the Pacific North-west, are among the largest fishes known. They may reach lengths of more than twelve feet and weigh well over a thousand pounds.

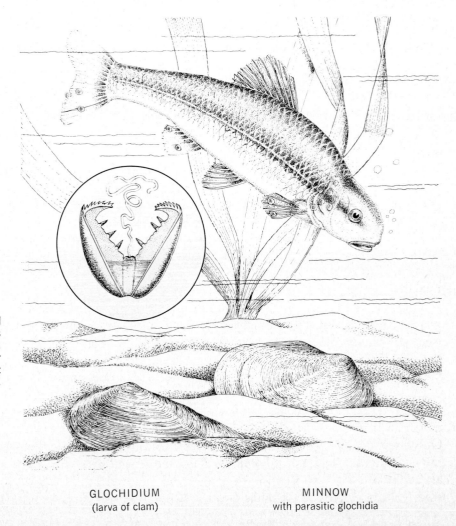

The **larvae of fresh-water clams and mussels** spend three to twelve weeks as parasites on the fins or gills of a fish. This stage is necessary for their survival; if they cannot find a host fish they will die.

GLOCHIDIUM
(larva of clam)

MINNOW
with parasitic glochidia

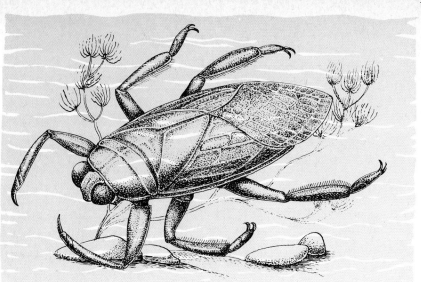

(left)
Giant water bugs, which may exceed two inches in length, will attack and kill even small fish. The males carry the eggs glued to their backs. Sometimes these insects are called "electric-light bugs," because they are attracted by artificial light.

Freshwater Clams

I N NEARLY ALL THE RIVERS—at least those that are unpolluted—large, dark-shelled mussels live. They are not closely related to salt-water mussels, but are more nearly like clams. They live in large bodies of standing or flowing water, and are almost never found in small brooks. Their presence may be noted by recognizing their tracks, looking like troughs, on the sandy bottom. They "walk" by putting out a long muscular "foot" which, when fully extended and dug into the sand, swells at its tip. The muscular action which would retract the foot if it were not firmly anchored then has the effect of drawing the animal's body forward. The mussel patiently "inches" itself forward by stops and starts in this way until it has covered a considerable distance.

Although mussels have no eyes, the edge of the mantle—a layer which builds up the shell and which lies just beneath it—is photosensitive, and if the animal is subjected to too much light the shells close tightly.

The blood of some mussels has a bluish tinge caused by a copper compound that provides the means by which the bloodstream distributes oxygen to the body. The blood is circulated by a heart, lying just beneath the hinge of the shells, which pumps slowly at a rate of about twenty pulses a minute.

Embryonic mussels do not leave the parent, but remain on the gills for a period of development. These are most peculiar larvae, and the part of their life cycle which brings them to maturity is quite involved. Once they leave the gills of the parent, they lie about at the bottom of the river waiting for a fish to swim by. They have two tiny shells that are equipped with large sharp teeth along the free edges. When a fish swims overhead, the little clamlike creature swims by snapping its shells

Clams move about by means of a muscular foot, which extends from the shell, digs into the sand and then swells at the tip. Thus anchored, the body moves forward to meet the foot. Fresh-water clams are comparable in size to their marine relatives, but their shells are lighter because lime salts are less plentiful in fresh-water. The dark lines on a shell indicate growth, but they cannot be used as accurate measurements of age.

wildly and clamps itself to some part of the fish. Within a day or so, the fish's skin has grown over the mussel larva, which is nourished by the fish's own body fluids. Anywhere from ten to thirty days later, the young mussel will break out and drop to the bottom of the river to begin its independent life. Fishes are not harmed by thus performing an essential role in the mussel's life cycle, and the mussel itself may live for as long as a dozen, or even fifteen, years if it does not fall prey to other creatures.

Mussels are sought as food by many animals. Turtles, otters, raccoons, minks and muskrats eat quantities of them, and at one time man harvested a great many to obtain shells for the "pearl" button industry. Most buttons are made of other materials nowadays, and the freshwater mussel is once more becoming abundant as a result. Pearls occasionally have been found in these animals, but so few of them are ever of any value that amateurs should be discouraged from digging them out of streams for this purpose.

Tiny Shrimps

Sandpipers may spend most of the year near streams, but they can get along on seacoasts and tidal flats during migrations.

In some streams, a gallon of water may contain upwards of a thousand tiny animals that are so small as to be nearly invisible. If a glass of water containing them is held to the light, small creatures will be seen swimming about with jerky motions. These are types of free-swimming shrimp, and they exist in such large numbers that they make up a large percentage of food for many water insects, clams and young fishes.

Large populations of microscopic shrimps live along the edge of a river, where aquatic vegetation grows abundantly. They can best be caught with a very fine-meshed net drawn through the water. If you examine the concentrate under a powerful magnifying glass you will see little at first, because the small animals hop and skip about actively; you might well find yourself, quite naturally, calling them by a name first given to them nearly 300 years ago: water fleas.

Water fleas, or cladocerans, are in fact very small shrimps which live within a transparent shell through which they stick a pair of oarlike antennae and a single kicking leg. Because of the transparency of their external structure, it is possible to see their internal organ systems quite clearly. The digestive system, for instance, can be traced from the mouth on through the body due to the volume of food which it contains. The small heart may be seen beating rapidly in the top half of the body. Anyone with a suitable microscope, if he is sufficiently skilled in its use, can study these creatures in detail. With adequate magnification and proper lighting it is possible to watch the action of the tiny heart. The blood is forced out of the front end and, because there are no special blood vessels as in our own bodies, blood cells can be seen circulating freely within the shrimp's body.

The cladoceran you watch will most likely be a female, for males appear only at certain times of the year—and even then may be uncommon. If the female is mature, you will probably notice young ones in the brood pouch on the animal's back. Strangely enough, these young water fleas have no father but are produced regularly by the female. Only when winter approaches do males appear to fertilize eggs which must last through the cold season.

"Invisible" Shrimps

T HERE IS ONE FAIRLY LARGE RIVER ANIMAL you are not likely to see, even if you look closely, for its invisibility is exceeded only by that of transparent jellyfishes. It is the well-named ghost shrimp. If a net is swept through river vegetation and along the bottom, ghost shrimps can sometimes be caught in large numbers. When one of these shrimps is placed in an aquarium and studied closely, its eyes and internal organs are its most visible structures. With a magnifying glass, however, small dots of pigmentation may be seen to cover the outer surface and, during the period of a day or two, these dots may quite noticeably change in size and arrangement. They are special cells which account for the protective resemblance of the shrimp to its background. The cells are of four types: white, red, yellow and blue, and the tint of the shrimp depends upon the arrangement and combination of these cells. Within a day after being placed in a new environment, a shrimp will take on the general hue of its background. The change is brought about by the action of a tiny gland situated on the eyestalk, for ghost shrimps have large hemispherical eyes with many lenses. These eyes protrude from the body on the end of a movable stalk.

When ghost shrimps are feeding quietly on the bottom, their many legs and appendages all seem to be performing different functions. Some, of course, support the animal and enable it to move about. Some sift through the mud and sand, while others transport food to the mouth parts which hold it and tear it apart. The food does not disappear once it is swallowed, but can be seen descending into the stomach.

Catfish

I N THE MURKY DEPTHS of sluggish streams and rivers where vision is unimportant in finding food, heavy-headed catfishes grope about the muddy bottom. Trailing beneath their mouths are long, whisker-like fleshy structures known as barbels; these barbels are sense organs and indicate to the scavenging catfish when it has passed over possible food. Then, with frantic twistings and turnings, the fish finds the morsel and bolts it down.

Small catfishes, or bullheads, closely resemble their larger relatives found in the greatest rivers. They eat insects, larvae, crayfishes and

Perhaps no bird is more at home in and under the water than the **dipper,** or water ouzel. With wings spread in the current, it walks along the bottom, completely submerged, to feed on small animals.

snails, and almost any bit of animal matter found on the bottom. Their sight is feeble and their eyes are so placed that the fish sees upward better than down along the bottom—so the barbels are of utmost importance in food-getting.

Catfishes spawn in the spring. Once the young have hatched, the adults convoy the small fishes about for a while. It is possible, if you are watching a clear spot in a river cove, to see a catfish swim by, surrounded by a cloud of tiny fishes.

One type of small catfish is not to be trifled with—the madtom. Madtoms look like other small catfishes, notably bullheads, but unlike these harmless animals, possess poison glands at the base of the paired front fins. If you are not careful, the spines arising from these fins can inflict a wound, which some people have described as being like a hornet sting —but more painful.

Odyssey of the Eel

"WHERE DO EELS SPAWN?" asked Aristotle, the world's first great biologist. When he could not find a satisfactory answer, he decided that eels did not reproduce, but merely grew up from mud and worms. It took twenty-two hundred years to answer the question. The delay was not caused by lack of interest, but every investigation failed until a Dane, Dr. Johann Schmidt, solved the riddle during the first quarter of this century.

Let us consider the North American eel—a long, black, slippery fish found in lakes, ponds, streams and brooks, that lives east of the Rocky Mountains. Eels also may be seen in brackish water; that is, water which is partly salt, as in estuaries and lower rivers. What is not commonly known is that the eels which ascend into fresh water are females, while the males remain in brackish water.

In the autumn, if we station ourselves near a barrier in a river such as a dam, or shallow, clear rapids, we might be rewarded with the sight of large eels swimming rapidly downstream. Sometimes eels are seen

Fresh-water eels that are one or two years old have a golden appearance, like the one in this picture. As they mature they turn brown-black; then they are ready to descend the rivers and streams, completing their life cycle in the ocean, where they spawn.

emerging from the water to wriggle in a snaky fashion over a short stretch of land which separates two bodies of water. Mature females, seven or more years old and several feet in length, work themselves through a maze of freshwater river systems until they emerge into bays and the open ocean. The males, too, leave their somewhat protected estuaries and bays and also head out. Where do they go?

Eels disappear from the sight of man once they reach the ocean. It seems certain that they swim by hidden routes, perhaps through submarine canyons, to one spot, and to one spot only. All these eels, from the coasts of the Atlantic, reach the same place in the Atlantic Ocean at nearly the same time. This region is close to the famed Sargasso Sea, and is north of the West Indies and south of Bermuda. Here the mature eels spawn and are never seen again. Their life cycle is complete.

Young eels look nothing like their parents. They are blade-shaped, and so transparent that you can look through them and see nothing more than a pair of staring eyes. In this form they swim weakly near the ocean surface, and undoubtedly are eaten in immense numbers. By the autumn of their first year, these tiny larval eels have reached the Atlantic coast, some going north, and some to the Caribbean and Gulf of Mexico. In these regions, or in bays, they change during the winter into miniature eels, called elvers. Later in the spring the fragile elvers swim against river currents and proceed upstream. The males remain in brackish waters, but the females fight their way into purely fresh waters, where they will live and grow for many years. During their first few years of life, eels are golden yellow, but as they mature and become ready for their long journey to the ocean, they turn a deep brown-black.

Next autumn, if you see a large eel swimming powerfully and rapidly down with the river current, think of the long journey in front of her, along the uncharted ocean floor. A year and a half later, on a fine spring day, you may sit beside a mill-dam and soak in the warming sun. At your feet, tiny ripples could reveal the frantic efforts of threadlike elvers to get through or over the dam into the security of the quiet waters beyond. These delicate creatures will be offspring of eels which left the coast over a year before. To reach the quiet inland waters they will have first had to fight their way through the perils of a thousand or more miles of ocean.

Once **elvers,** or immature eels, enter fresh water, they burrow beneath the bottom sand. There they remain hidden, only their heads protruding for breathing and finding food.

Sick Rivers

I F WE COMPARE A RIVER with a living organism, we must include what happens to all life at one time or another—sickness. Young brooks and mature rivers may suddenly be afflicted by troubles for which there is no speedy cure. These difficulties are only rarely due to natural causes, such as the leaching of certain minerals from the soil; in nearly all cases they arise because of man's thoughtlessness or carelessness. The principal sickness of rivers and streams is expressed in a simple word—pollution.

When you are travelling in a train and happen to look out the window, you may follow a trackside stream with idle thoughts until it suddenly turns a brilliant yellow or some equally unexpected hue. The cause is nearly always close at hand in the form of drains or settling basins which lead out directly from factories and processing plants. This type of pollution is startling, and usually it leads to fairly effective protests by those who care about the destruction of our natural amenities. Unfortunately, most kinds of destructive pollution do not advertise themselves so blatantly, so they can persist for a long time and become progressively worse before the sickness is recognized and diagnosed. Frequently, the wastes poured into the stream may be invisible; they may give rise to no unpleasant stench, and cause no immediate destruction of animal life. Instead, aquatic creatures sicken gradually and die—or simply desert the affected area for good. Years later, highly trained teams of scientists may discover that a tiny trickle from some small mill or factory has been the cause of transforming the stream from a heavily-populated environment into one barren of all life—into a liquid desert. The correction of such a situation requires a great deal of money and much time. Poisoned rivers do not recover overnight, and when the animals have been absent for long, it will take many years for them to become established once more.

The restoration of polluted rivers to a healthy condition is a difficult task. Many scientific organizations are working ceaselessly on such problems; often with little success. A large factory cannot be made to change its method of production overnight, although some mills that have saved their wastes from nearby rivers have found unexpected profits through producing and selling by-products in the form of chemicals and fertilizers.

Just as there are preventive and curative practices in medicine, so there are, too, in keeping our rivers healthy. The cure of sickness is always important; but it is far better to prevent the illness from arising. Therefore, as new factories are built, efficient methods of waste disposal should be incorporated in their manufacturing processes to keep local rivers uncontaminated.

It should be realized, too, that factories are not the only sources of pollution. Owners of private lands have been responsible for much damage. Improper run-off of water over farm fields will erode the topsoil so valuable to the gardener and farmer; this is carried away downstream where it settles over animals and plants living on the stream bottom and suffocates them. Known as siltation, this causes an enormous amount of harm in some of our streams.

Then there are the biological wastes—sewage, run-off from garbage dumps and drainage from cattle watering holes. Wood pulp factories,

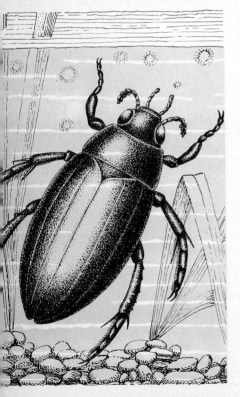

As long as the **diving beetle,** or "water tiger," has plenty of food, it seems content. One was kept alive in captivity for over three years, being fed on bits of raw meat.

(far left)
Dragonfly nymphs adapt to their watery world in several ways. Some crawl about, some burrow; others like this one, sprawl on the bottom of ponds and streams.

(left)
More than three thousand species of **midge larvae** are known to inhabit all types of fresh and brackish water, living in the muddy bottoms. Often they are brilliantly tinted, due to a pigment similar to the one in our blood.

slaughter houses and poultry processing plants at times have all contributed to stream pollution. In general, organic wastes announce their presence fairly quickly by their offensive smell—and those people who live close by are apt to insist on a quick return to a saner method of waste disposal.

If you are not struck by the importance of river pollution, stop by one of these unfortunate streams long enough to understand what has happened. Watch the grey sludge pass by the bank on which you stand. In all the vast expanse of water before you, the only active life under the surface is likely to be bacterial. The only fishes you see float by, belly up, are dead by suffocation and poisoning.

This gloomy discussion may seem out of place in a **chapter** about the life of rivers; however, *no* life occurs in a really sick stream—and healthy streams can be made ill. With more people understanding the problem and working toward a solution, there need be no more polluted rivers, and those that are sick can be cured. You may be able to help.

Living Things Help a River Recover

A<small>S POLLUTION CONTINUES DOWNSTREAM</small>, it becomes more dissolved and therefore not as poisonous to animals and plants. Then various small forms of life begin to carpet the bottom of the river. A few species of animals are able to tolerate the still-dangerous condition of the water; most of these are either tube-dwelling worms or insect larvae.

Like their large relative the earthworm, tube-dwelling worms, or tubificids, devour great quantities of sediment and mud. This material is passed through their digestive systems and deposited as castings about the tube burrows. The overturn which results aerates the mud and provides opportunities for other forms of aquatic life to become established. Tubificids are one of the basic cures for the rehabilitation of sick rivers. When these worms are found in a polluted stream it is a sign that a return to reasonably good health may have begun.

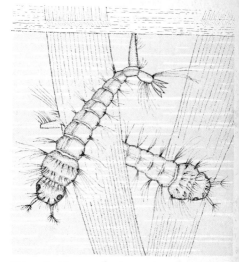

Mosquito bites can be dangerous in some areas of the world, for malaria or yellow fever may result. In temperate regions, however, mosquitos are mostly regarded as simple nuisances. At the **larva** and **pupa** stages, the insects live underwater, breathing air through their tails.

Sometimes on a summer evening, tiny, delicate, flying insects will appear from nowhere to fill the air with a gentle buzzing; these are the midges. Their swarms, often seen near water, sometimes contain so many insects that they form swaying clouds. While you may swat and scratch when you have to pass through such a cloud, usually there is no reason, since nearly all species of midges are incapable of biting. When great masses of these insects fly about, you may wonder where they came from and where the young could have grown so well hidden. Like many other flying insects, the larvae are seen by few people, for they dwell in the bottom mud of streams and rivers.

Midge larvae, although they are rarely seen outside their muddy environment, often are brilliantly tinted; some are deep red because of a pigment similar to the red haemoglobin of our own blood. Pigments such as these enable oxygen to be carried about by the bloodstreams of animals.

Midge larvae are plant eaters, although bits of decaying matter are also eaten. Some forms spin nets across the mouth of the tube and trap food particles carried along in the stream. They eat the enmeshed food—net and all—and then spin a new net! The complete operation may take only a few minutes, and it happens dozens of times in a single day.

There are over 3,000 different kinds of midges, and many of these species live in enormous concentrations. The larvae have been known to reach populations of over 50,000 per square yard of bottom mud. These heavy concentrations mean that an immense amount of food material is sifted out of the stream. As midge larvae are some of the few animals that can live in polluted water, much of the dead and decaying

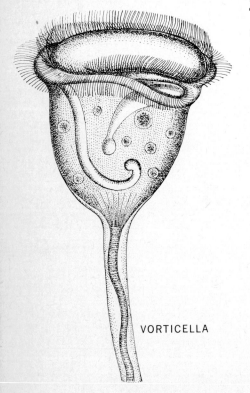

VORTICELLA

Microscopic animals
found in a drop of fresh water

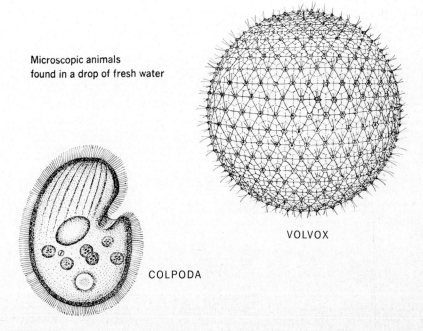

COLPODA

VOLVOX

matter that results from the pollution is caught and eaten. In fact these larvae can be considered a valuable acquisition in a badly poisoned stream, because they can be of great help in cleaning it. They are usually found in the "recovery zone" of such rivers in greater numbers than in clean, unpolluted streams.

They are of great value in another way, too; for no other insect or insect larva is eaten in such large quantities by freshwater fishes. The stomachs of some fishes, and particularly of those which feed along the bottom, often are packed tight with these small creatures.

Because this chapter concerns upland brooks and streams, rivers and areas of pollution, there is no further space to tell of the mighty river estuaries which flow into the sea. These great bodies of water, widening into bays, are worthy of consideration by themselves.

The Living River

IN THE CHAPTER you have just completed, you have read about animals typical of brooks and rivers. Many creatures in nearby streams are not even mentioned, and some of those described here are likely to be absent from your own brook. All bodies of flowing water resemble one another, but each proves to be in some way unique when it is studied very closely.

Many conditions affect the population of a stream, and these conditions are never found in equal force in two different streams. The streams' origins may differ considerably: one brook may start with rainwater gathered from a sloping watershed, while another may erupt into being from an underground spring. A stream, through passing close by a town or city in the early part of its long journey to the sea, may lose its natural health almost at once. Others may be tinted by the earth washed from their banks. Some rivers are clear; some are so opaque that visibility is limited to an inch below the surface. No two streams are alike.

It will be for you to study and to learn about the brook, creek, or river nearest you. If you are fortunate, you will have a pleasant brook

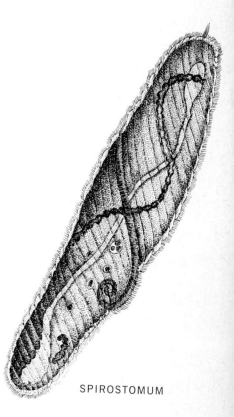

SPIROSTOMUM

PARAMECIUM

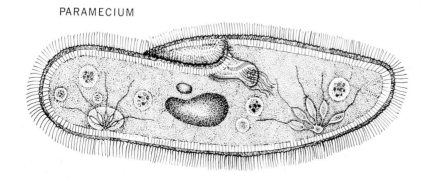

within walking distance, and your education into the complexities of its life probably began years ago when you first sat alone by its edge. You can further your understanding and appreciation of the stream by constructing a few simple pieces of collecting apparatus and by looking even more closely.

Rocks and sticks overturned may yield a few specimens you have never seen before; so might a few holes dug into the shoreline. Fine-meshed nets on the ends of long poles usually capture many of the swimming animals when the net is swept slowly upstream. A wire tray made out of screening is useful, too. Hold it in a narrow part of the brook while someone else a few yards upstream lifts rock and creates a disturbance. All the small hidden creatures exposed to the current will be swept downstream and lodged against the screen for your examination.

One last word of caution: streams are a natural heritage. Too few are pure, healthy and well-populated with the animals described here. Learn all you can about the brooks and rivers near you, but do not thoughtlessly or deliberately destroy or over-collect the animals and plants in them. Some of the animals, particularly larval insects, make good aquarium specimens—if you feed them properly and keep the water clean and aerated. Many of the larger animals, such as frogs, salamanders, snakes and turtles require so much food and such a well-balanced environment that you would be unwise to try to keep them for more than a couple of days. Fishes, in general, should never be removed from streams. Indeed, it is unlawful to catch any of the species regarded as game *except* by hook and line.

Frontiers still exist in our own communities. Any stream is capable of yielding information which is entirely new to science, whether it concerns the flowing water itself or the life contained within.

Explore the stream near your home!

Among the largest of all reptiles, **crocodiles** are common residents of some of the larger streams in tropical areas. They feed on whatever they can get hold of—including each other!

To MANY PEOPLE, the mere thought of insects evokes a negative response, and the sight of one is liable to induce an almost automatic, sometimes frantic, attempt to swat, squash or spray it. Even those who profess to love nature often draw the line at certain insects, particularly those that bite or sting, attack favorite plants or get into clothes, cupboards and beds. Of course, because of their astronomical numbers, it is difficult to ignore them, but that is exactly what most of us would *like* to do. A closer look at these creatures will prove this attitude wrong.

While some insects may be considered harmful to man, most are beneficial or at least neutral. Moreover, since they are the prey of many birds, fishes and other animals, they are vital links in nature's food chains. That is why eradication campaigns that kill both helpful or neutral insects along with pests generally do more harm than good, and this damage is further compounded when chemical insecticides move up the food chains, poisoning higher animals, including people. Selective biological controls are probably the only real solutions.

Yet for our interest and delight alone, insects are worthy of closer examination, To enter, as in the chapter that follows, THE WORLD OF INSECTS, is to find oneself among the most varied group of animals that exists, with over 850,000 species, endless color combinations and forms, and fascinating differences in habits and life histories. Covered here are the broad subjects of growth, feeding, defense, sensory perception, and others, with examples from both familiar and lesser-known insects.

There is little doubt that the most popular insects are those taken up in BUTTERFLIES AND MOTHS. While the adults, quite properly, are prized for their beauty and delicacy, the caterpillars also deserve, and receive, our attention. This chapter provides an opportunity to learn more about common species and, at the same time, to become acquainted with some of the more fabulous and rarer ones.

Since enough is usually said, if not known, about insects that are pests, the balance may be set aright by the final chapter on OUR INSECT ALLIES. These fall into several groups: those that are parasites on harmful insects; those that prey on pests; scavengers that enrich the soil and improve sanitation; pollinators; weed destroyers; and producers of useful substances like silk, shellac, honey and beeswax.

INSECTS

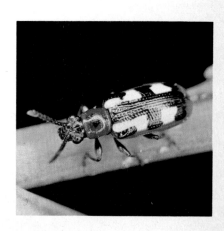

► *The astounding array of animals that walk on six legs or fly with four wings.*

World of Insects

As this chapter is about insects, let us first decide exactly what an insect is; this is necessary because many people's ideas on the subject are rather imprecise.

There is a great division or *Phylum* of the animal kingdom called the *Arthropoda*. It includes such creatures as crabs, lobsters, woodlice, spiders, scorpions, centipedes, millipedes—and insects. The most important feature of all these animals is the possession of a hard, jointed skeleton, which encases the body and limbs. This seems a strange idea to us because our skeletons are internal, but it is a fact that the jointed "shell" of a lobster's or a beetle's leg plays the same part as the bones in a man's leg. The muscles are attached to the different segments and, by contracting, cause them to pivot on their joints to make the complicated movements necessary for walking. The difference is that in the arthropod the skeleton has the form of a hard tube containing the muscles, while in a man (or any other vertebrate animal) it consists of rods of bone surrounded by the muscles. In insects the skeleton consists mainly of two substances, chitin and sclerotin, the latter forming the hard outer layer.

Woodlice, centipedes, millipedes and spiders, then, are included with the insects in the *Phylum Arthropoda*; but they are not insects, and we shall have nothing more to say about them.

The insects differ from the other arthropods mainly in the following two characteristics: when they are adult their bodies are divided into three distinct parts—head, thorax (or chest) and abdomen (or hindbody)—and they never have more than three pairs of legs. In addition,

Sometimes insect life seems to be more strictly organized than human society. Many bees and ants have complicated systems in which tasks are divided among queen, worker, and sometimes warrior. The life histories of solitary insects such as butterflies also follow rather rigid patterns: from an egg the caterpillar hatches; from the caterpillar the chrysalis develops; and from the chrysalis emerges the delicate butterfly. Another life style is illustrated by the **oil beetle** (top right), whose larva lives as a parasite in the nests of solitary bees. If threatened, this wingless beetle discharges an unpleasant-smelling liquid from its joints.

most adult insects possess one or two pairs of wings while no other arthropods have them; the legs and wings are always attached to the thorax. If you examine a wasp you will see that it conforms very closely to this typical insect pattern. A scientist who is a specialist in the study of insects is called an entomologist.

Those Latin Names

THE LATIN OR SCIENTIFIC NAMES of animals may seem rather cumbersome and unpronounceable until you get used to them, but they are essential. The number of different kinds of insects that have received them is already over 850,000 and of these only a minute fraction are known by names at all in the everyday speech of any country.

In addition, the Latin names are international. The butterfly which is known to entomologists of every nation as *Nymphalis antiopa* is called Camberwell beauty in Great Britain and *Trauermantel* in Germany, and in America a translation of the German name is used, mourning cloak. It inhabits numerous other countries and must be known under a large number of other names as well. The adoption of one name to be used everywhere by people who are interested in insects obviously simplifies the exchange of information between entomologists of different nationalities.

In this Latin system of naming, each species or "kind" of animal or plant is known by two names: a specific one, which identifies it, and a generic name, which defines its closest relationship with other species. A group of animals included under one generic name is called a genus (plural, genera); the word species is the same in singular and plural. The name of the genus is put first, that of the species second—just as "John Smith" is printed "Smith, John" in a directory.

To illustrate the system let us take a familiar insect, the small white, or cabbage, butterfly, *Pieris rapae,* whose caterpillars feed on cabbages

(above)
This inch-long North American bug, often called an "electric light bug," is attracted to artificial light. It is a **giant water beetle,** whose tropical relatives measure up to four inches in length.

(right)
Known as the Camberwell beauty in Britain, this dark yet colorful butterfly is called **mourning cloak** in the United States. Because of such variations in names from one area or country to another, the scientific (Latin) names are best for making positive identifications.

almost all over the world. The first name indicates its close relationship with the large white, *Pieris brassicae,* the green-veined white or mustard white, *Pieris napi,* and others which are placed in the genus *Pieris.* The combination of the two names identifies the butterfly precisely; that is to say no other animal, anywhere in the world, can have the scientific name *Pieris rapae.* This is not the case with English names: peacock can refer to a bird or a butterfly, and English-speaking people in India use the name bluebottle, not for a fly, but for a very beautiful butterfly, *Graphium sarpedon.*

In the complete system of classification of animals the insects form a class of the *Phylum Arthropoda,* and are divided in their turn into a number of orders; all of the beetles form one order and all butterflies and moths another. Here is a list of the orders of insects of which members are mentioned.

A large, predatory insect, the **praying mantis** catches its prey with its spined fore legs, which it holds up in an attitude suggestive of prayer. The mantid shown in this picture is an inhabitant of the southern United States.

Silverfish and Bristletails (*Thysanura*). Small, primitive insects without wings.

Cockroaches and Mantises (*Dictyoptera*).

Termites (*Isoptera*). Social insects allied to cockroaches and having a superficial resemblance to ants.

Stick-insects and Leaf-insects (*Phasmidae*). Mostly rather large insects, often exhibiting remarkable camouflage.

Grasshoppers and Crickets (*Saltatoria*). The hind legs are enlarged for jumping.

Earwigs (*Dermaptera*).

Caddis flies (*Trichoptera*). Pass their early stages in the water; the larvae construct little cases to live in.

Dragonflies and Damselflies (*Odonata*). Large insects with two pairs of wings, which pass their early stages in the water.

Bugs (*Hemiptera*). The mouthparts are adapted for piercing and sucking and there are usually two pairs of wings, of which the front pair are thick or leathery in some bugs, forming a cover for the hind pair; shield-bugs, aphids, cicadas.

Butterflies and Moths (*Lepidoptera*). The four wings are covered with minute tinted scales which often form beautiful patterns.

Flies (*Diptera*). Insects with one pair of delicate transparent wings.

Wasps, Bees and Ants (*Hymenoptera*). Usually two pairs of delicate transparent wings; in ants the males and females have wings but the workers are wingless.

Beetles (*Coleoptera*). The largest order; usually there are two pairs of wings, but the front pair is transformed to horny sheaths which cover and protect the hind wings.

Perhaps you have found this first section rather heavy going? There is no need to remember it all, but refer to it from time to time while reading the rest of the subject.

How Insects Grow

Its resemblance to the much larger animal has given the **rhinoceros beetle** its name. The curved horns that the male wears on his head and thorax make him look more menacing than he really is. Found in the southern United States, the species pictured here has a curious, blotchy pattern on most of its skeleton.

An external skeleton gives an animal a number of advantages. For one thing, besides acting as a skeleton for attachment of the muscles, it turns the animal into an "ironclad". For another, it prevents loss of water by evaporation; this is very important for small animals who would otherwise be quickly desiccated in dry conditions. But there is one great drawback; the outer skeleton can stretch very little, and it does not grow with the animal, as our bones do. The relation of an insect to its skin or skeleton is rather like that of a schoolboy to his clothes; from time to time, as the animal grows, the outer covering becomes intolerably tight and has to be discarded for a new suit. When an insect sheds its outgrown outer covering a new one has always already formed underneath. At first this is soft and stretches easily, but it soon hardens, and further growth must wait for the next shedding. There must be many parents who would be very happy if the growth of schoolboys followed the same pattern.

The simplest sort of insect life history is that of the silverfish, *Lepisma saccharina*. This is a little wingless insect that is found living in houses in most countries, usually in warm cupboards in the kitchen. It is very primitive—that is to say it resembles the evolutionary ancestors of all insects, which lived many millions of years ago. The female lays eggs, and from these hatch tiny silverfishes that differ from their parents only in size. They feed, just as the adults do, on starchy or sugary substances, and shed their outer cases repeatedly as they grow. When they reach a certain size they mate and lay eggs, and continue to grow and to renew their skeletons at intervals after they have started breeding; a silverfish may make use of as many as fifty skeletons during its whole lifetime.

The life history of a grasshopper is rather different. The insect which hatches from the egg is not unlike a tiny, stumpy grasshopper, but it has no wings at all. Five to eight times, in the course of growing up, it sheds the outer casing, not only of its body, but of its legs and antennae as well. After the first or second shedding, the wings appear as little pads or flaps, and with each following change they become larger relative to the size of the insect, until finally they are completely developed and the grasshopper can fly. At this stage it is able to breed, is fully grown, and no longer needs to change its outer skeleton. Here again the feeding habits of the insect are the same throughout its life. Bugs also have a life history of this kind.

The third main type of insect life history is well shown by that of a butterfly. Here the small creature that hatches from the egg is quite unlike a butterfly. It is a little wormlike creature that we call a caterpillar or larva. The larva feeds on leaves and grows rapidly; its "skin" is far softer and more flexible than that of most insects, but it sheds its covering several times nevertheless. In preparation, the caterpillar spins a mat of silk on a leaf and fastens its rearmost legs to it. Then the covering behind the head splits and the insect crawls out of its old "skin", which remains anchored to the silken mat.

When it is fully grown, the caterpillar hangs itself up with threads of silk and remains without moving for a day or two. This time, when the old covering is slipped off, there appears not just another larger caterpillar but a pupa or chrysalis. While the larva hangs by its silken threads a most extraordinary process takes place. All its muscles and most of its internal organs dissolve into a kind of living soup, which then re-forms into those of a butterfly. The chrysalis is really a complete butterfly, packed away into a hard capsule.

After a period of several weeks or months the final shedding takes place. The skin of the pupa splits and the butterfly crawls out. At first its wings are like little crumpled bags, but body fluid is pumped into them, causing them to expand, and is then withdrawn, so that they flatten to form the broad patterned wings of the beautiful perfect insect. Take a paper bag that has been crumpled up into a ball (but not torn), find the opening and blow gently into it until the bag is inflated. Then let the air out and carefully press the bag into the flat, square shape it had when it was new. This operation illustrates very well how the wings of a butterfly are expanded and then flattened when it emerges from the chrysalis.

In this case the three different stages, after the egg, look like three wholly different animals, and all behave quite differently. The caterpillar crawls about and devours leaves; the chrysalis neither feeds nor moves at all; and the butterfly flies in the air and feeds by sucking the nectar of flowers through a hollow tube or proboscis.

The change of form that takes place in the life history of an insect is called its metamorphosis. In the case of the silverfish there is no metamorphosis; the grasshopper's life gives an example of incomplete, the butterfly's of complete, metamorphosis. The kind of metamorphosis they undergo is an important feature in the classification of insects. In the list of orders of insects, the last four, from butterflies and moths onwards, undergo complete metamorphosis; in the rest, metamorphosis is partial or (in the *Thysanura*) absent.

The time that insects take to complete their growth varies widely. In general, the warmer the climate, the faster growth proceeds; most butterflies in the tropics develop from egg to perfect insect in three weeks or so, while in temperate climates many of them take a year, and appear on the wing regularly at a certain season. In northern regions, not far from the Arctic Circle, many of the larger insects take two years to complete their life cycle. The North American

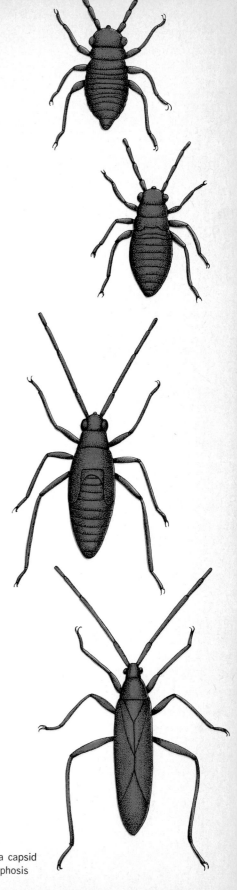

Four stages in the development of a capsid bug, showing incomplete metamorphosis

Complete **metamorphosis**—the change in form undergone by many animals—is illustrated by the life history of any butterfly, such as this European **swallowtail.** The larva, or caterpillar, that emerges from the egg grows to full size, and then it turns into a chrysalis. After some weeks or months the skin of the chrysalis splits and the butterfly crawls out, spreads its crumpled wings and flies away.

Butterflies and moths never eat solid food. They lack the strong, biting jaws of other insects, but have instead a long tube, or **proboscis,** through which they suck up nectar and other fluids. When not in use, the proboscis is curled up out of the way. Feeding here is a brilliantly colored **Urania moth** from East Africa.

periodical cicada (*Magicicada septendecim*) feeds underground in its early stages and takes an astonishing seventeen years to mature.

How Insects Feed

Y OU CAN USUALLY FORM SOME IDEA of what any animal feeds on by looking at its teeth; the teeth of cats and dogs are designed for tearing and cutting flesh, those of horses work like grindstones, enabling the animal to feed on grass and hay, while anteaters have no teeth at all. The same is true of insects, though their mouth-parts are very different from those of vertebrate animals.

The first thing to notice is that an insect's jaws work sideways, not up and down like our own. A cockroach, which has quite typical insect mouth-parts, has two pairs of jaws, the strong and hard mandibles, which are the real biting apparatus, and the maxillae, each of which has a little jointed finger called a palp. The maxillae (maxilla in the singular) are used mainly for manipulating the food and pushing it into the mouth; you can think of it as a sort of paired tongue. Also there is an upper lip called the labrum and a lower one called the labium.

This sort of equipment enables an insect to eat almost any solid food and to suck up liquids with the lips and maxillae. Cockroaches will feed on anything we eat ourselves, and on a great many other things, too. All those insects that live by chewing up leaves, grass and wood have mouth-parts of this kind; these include locusts and grass-hoppers, caterpillars and termites. The mouth-parts of those insects that prey on other forms of animal life, ants, wasps, dragonflies and many kinds of beetles, are also of this type.

A totally different sort of feeding apparatus is seen in the butterflies and moths; these insects never eat at all. They only drink, and their jaws have disappeared altogether. Instead they have a long tube through which they suck up liquids, such as the nectar of flowers. This tongue or proboscis is really a most wonderful instrument. It is very long and slender and quite flexible, so that it can be curled up like the hairspring of a watch and packed away, when not in use, between two little projections on the front of the head. The convolvulus

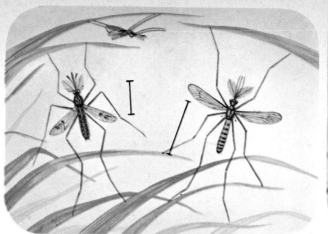

hawkmoth, *Herse convolvuli,* a species found all over the Old World and Australia, has a proboscis whose length is slightly more than the insect's wing-span of four and one-half to five inches. It is interesting to note that in the stages of their life history butterflies and moths are equipped with two totally different types of mouth-parts; the caterpillar has biting jaws, the adult, or perfect insect, a slender sucking tube and no jaws at all.

The only other large group of insects that feed in this way are the bees, which are also seekers of nectar. Their tubular "tongues" are of a rather different form from those of butterflies and far shorter. And the adult bee retains its jaws, which it uses for shaping wax.

The third important mode of insect feeding can be described as the piercing and sucking method, and it is particularly characteristic of the bugs. In everyday speech this short expressive word may be applied to almost any insect; but entomologists confine its use to the order *Hemiptera.* Bugs are very diverse in appearance; they may look rather like beetles, as for example the shield-bugs, or like four-winged flies, ranging in size from the tiny aphids or green-flies to the big noisy cicadas. All bugs, however, whatever their appearance, have a feeding apparatus that acts rather like a hypodermic syringe when it is used as a suction pump to take a blood sample.

When a bug is closely examined it appears to have a beak projecting from the front of its head. This is really the protecting sheath in which the effective piercing and sucking mouth-parts are contained; these consist of two pairs of very fine, needle-like stylets. The stylets are extremely sharp, and they also fit together to form a slender double tube through which the insect sucks up its liquid meal. The great majority of bugs feed on the sap of plants; but a few, including the notorious and disgusting bed-bug, are blood-suckers.

The other insects that feed in this way are some of the true flies or *Diptera;* of these the mosquitoes and biting midges are familiar to everyone. While most of the bugs are sap feeders the majority of the so-called "biting" flies are blood-suckers, and it is this habit of feeding that makes them the most dangerous of all the insect enemies of man. The actual bite of these insects is seldom more than an irritation, but

(top left)
Most of the insects that are properly called bugs feed by sucking the sap of plants, but flies that feed in this way, such as **mosquitoes** and **biting midges**, are blood-suckers. After piercing the skin with their sharp "beaks," they inject some saliva to prevent the blood from clotting and then suck up their meal. The swelling and irritation are caused by the saliva, which also can spread disease—such as malaria or yellow fever—if the insect is infected. It is worth noting that only the female mosquito bites, never the male.

(top right)
Because of its method of feeding, the **house-fly** and its relatives help to spread many dangerous diseases. It first dissolves its food in some of the liquid contents of its stomach by throwing up on it. Then it mops up its meal with its proboscis. In this way it may transfer dirt or sewage on which it has recently fed to a person's plate.

Bumblebees are attractive insects with tubular "tongues" for sucking nectar and jaws for shaping wax. They are found mostly in the temperate parts of the world. Shown here, feeding on a thistle flower, is a North American species, *Bombus americanorum.*

Among the most numerous of all insects are the **aphids,** which do great damage to plants by sucking their sap and spreading disease. It is easy to understand why they are so common: a single female can have millions of offspring in a year.

as conveyors of disease they are responsible for the ill health and death of millions of people.

The most widely spread and damaging of all are the malaria-carrying mosquitoes, which all belong to one genus called *Anopheles.* The common mosquitoes of the genus *Culex* cannot convey malaria and are not carriers of any prevalent disease; but those of a third genus, *Aedes,* carry yellow fever. Only female mosquitoes drink blood; the males feed innocently on the nectar or sap of plants.

To understand how these insects convey disease we need to study their mode of feeding. When a mosquito alights on your skin it runs the incredibly fine stylets of its mouth-parts into a small blood vessel and first injects a little saliva, which prevents the blood from coagulating or clotting in the hair-fine sucking tube. It is this saliva which causes the swelling and irritation of the bite. If the mosquito is infected with the germs of malaria or the virus of yellow fever some of these will be squirted in with the saliva; if the person bitten is already infected, the mosquito will suck the disease organisms in with its meal of blood, and so convey the disease to some future victim of its bite.

The sap-sucking bugs feed in the same way and play exactly the same role among plants. Potato blight is carried by a kind of aphid, *Myzus persicae,* and the beet-leaf bug, *Piesma quadratum,* carries the serious leaf-crinkle disease of sugar beet.

A fourth method of feeding is used by the house-fly and its relatives. These flies have a proboscis ending in a little pad, and they feed by mopping up exposed liquids or soluble substances such as sugar, which they dissolve by regurgitating part of the liquid contents of their stomachs on it. This rather revolting mode of feeding causes flies to be dangerous disease carriers, since they are apt to feed on any sort of dirt or sewage and then transfer their attention to a plate of cakes or a bowl of sugar. In communities that are ignorant of hygiene or careless about protecting their food from flies, diseases like dysentery are very prevalent, and are largely fly-borne.

Continued in Volume 8

CREDITS
Color photographs and illustrations appearing in this volume were supplied by the following: Photo Researchers, Inc.; The American Museum of Natural History; Armando Curcio; Doubleday & Company, Inc.; U.S. Department of the Interior, National Park Service; and H. S. Stuttman Co., Inc.

Cover illustration and illustration on page 835 were photographed at The American Museum of Natural History.